ELEMENTARY CHEMISTRY

NOTES
(REVISED)

COLES EDITORIAL BOARD

ISBN 0-7740-3709-1

© COPYRIGHT 1986 AND PUBLISHED BY
COLES PUBLISHING COMPANY LIMITED
TORONTO — CANADA
PRINTED IN CANADA

Manufactured by Webcom Limited
Cover finish: Webcom's Exclusive **Duracoat**

CONTENTS

1. STATES OF MATTER

MATTER

The term matter is used for any of the different kinds of materials in the world around us. Examples are rock, wood, oil, water, air and so on. There are three physical states of matter:

Solid, Liquid, Gas

Water, a liquid, also exists in the solid state as ice, and as water vapor in the gaseous state.

The actual physical state of a substance depends on the temperature and pressure conditions. Examples: candle wax is solid at room temperature but melts to liquid if put in boiling water. Chlorine is a gas at room conditions, but changes to liquid if cooled and compressed.

SOLIDS

A solid is rigid because of strong forces of attraction between the particles. Each particle is vibrating within its own definite location in the solid and the particles are not free to move through the solid. It follows that a particle always has the same nearest neighbor particles around it. A solid occupies a definite region in space and has definite boundary surfaces. The particles are closely packed so that there is a balance of the electrical forces of attraction and repulsion. For this reason solids greatly resist forces which tend to push the particles closer together or to pull them apart.

LIQUIDS

These are non-rigid or fluid, and may be poured. A liquid takes the shape of the container and has a definite upper boundary surface. Each particle does not always have the same nearest neighbor particles because as well as vibrating, the particles may slip and slide around each other. Forces of cohesion are strong enough to keep the particles from flying apart, and as in solids the particles are closely packed and resist compression forces. Liquids exert a pressure because of their weight and this pressure increases with depth.

GASES

The forces of cohesion in gases are very weak and become important only when the molecules are being squeezed close together. Like liquids, gases are fluid. As well as vibrating, the particles are rotating and moving in straight lines. They exert pressure on striking any surface. On the average the particles are very far apart compared to the size of the individual molecules, and for this reason gases may be greatly compressed. The boundary surface of a gas is simply the inner surface of the container.

CRYSTALS

These are sometimes called true solids. Examples are sodium chloride (common salt), naphthalene (moth flakes), and sugar. In a crystal the particles are arranged in a regular repeating patter so that distances between particles are constant. On growing crystals from solution we find typical external features, flat surface faces, definite shape, and constant angles between straight edges.

Some solids are classed as non-crystalline or amorphous. Examples are glass, rosin, polythene. They have the typical irregular particle arrangement of a liquid but are rigid like crystals. On breaking a block of an amorphous solid, the surfaces and edges are found to be curved.

CHANGE OF STATE

This is caused by heating or cooling a substance, or by increasing or decreasing the pressure.

Any pure crystalline solid which does not decompose on heating will melt at its own characteristic melting temperature.

Examples — ice melts to water at $0^{\circ}C$ and solid naphthalene becomes liquid at $80^{\circ}C$.

Melting, Fusion, Liquefaction are words used for the change of state from solid to liquid.

Because of pressure effects on melting point, it is defined as the temperature at which a solid becomes liquid if the pressure is standard. Standard pressure supports a column of mercury 760 mm long in a simple mercury barometer.

Freezing or Solidification are terms for the change of state from liquid to solid. A pure liquid has a definite freezing point defined as the temperature at which it becomes solid when the pressure is standard.

The freezing point of a liquid is the same as the melting point of its solid form. Example: water freezes at $0^{\circ}C$, and ice melts at $0^{\circ}C$.

Most liquids left in the open gradually disappear. This is called evaporation. Individual molecules break loose from the surface layer and enter the air.

At the boiling temperature many high energy molecules within a liquid push to form bubbles of vapor which rise and escape. Boiling Point is the temperature at which bubbles of vapor freely escape from a liquid when the pressure is standard. At boiling point the vapor must exert enough pressure to overcome the downward pressure of the air. Therefore boiling point may be defined as the temperature at which the vapor pressure of a liquid equals standard atmospheric pressure.

Variations of vapor pressure with temperature are discussed on page 36. When vapors are cooled or compressed they condense to liquids.

Sublimation: Solids such as naphthalene or benzoic acid gradually disappear if exposed to air. Molecules escape from the surface of the crystal and go straight to the vapor state. The term sublimation is also used for the reverse change when molecules of vapor unite to form a solid without first becoming a liquid. Examples: iodine crystals sublime to a violet vapor if gently heated. In below zero temperatures water vapor forms solid frost by sublimation.

EXPERIMENT TO MEASURE MELTING POINT

Melting point tubes are about 3 inches long and as thick as a pencil lead. They are made by drawing out soft heated soda glass. One end of the tube is sealed, and some finely powdered naphthalene crystals are scooped into the tube. If it is gently scraped with a file the powder moves to the bottom. The tube is attached to a thermometer as shown and slowly heated in a beaker of water which is being constantly stirred. At the melting point the white crystals change sharply to a colorless liquid.

A pure solid melts sharply within a degree range of temperature. Impure solids such as candle wax melt over a larger temperature range. Because melting point is a definite physical property of a solid it may be used to identify a substance. For example, two solids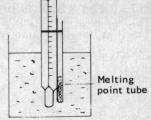

Melting point tube

may look alike and melt at the same temperature. If samples are mixed and a mixed melting point is taken we find that the melting temperature of the mixture is lower if the solids differ, but if both samples are the same substance the melting point does not change.

EXPERIMENT TO MEASURE FREEZING POINT

A thermometer is put in a test tube which is then half filled with flakes of naphthalene or phenol or candle wax. The solid is melted by heating the test tube in a beaker of boiling water. Then the test tube is quickly clamped to a stand and a large empty beaker is put around it as a shield from air drafts. Without disturbing the thermometer the temperature of the cooling liquid is noted every minute until there is no further change. A graph of temperature against time may be plotted as shown below.

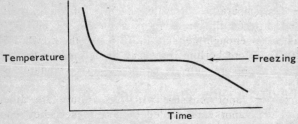

The freezing point corresponds to the flat portion of the cooling curve. In the case of an impure solid such as candle wax which is a mixture of several hydrocarbon waxes, there is not one definite freezing temperature. Sometimes a liquid will supercool below its usual freezing point especially if it is not disturbed. Then adding a single small "seed" crystal of the solid or moving the thermometer in the liquid suddenly starts solidification.

EXPERIMENT TO MEASURE BOILING POINT

The apparatus is similar to that used in taking melting points except that a small test tube (7 cm) is attached to the thermometer by a rubber band. The tube is half filled with a liquid such as carbon tetrachloride or methanol and an open piece of capillary tubing is dropped into the liquid. The thermometer and tube is gradually heated in a beaker of stirred water. A steady stream of vapor bubbles rise from the sharp edges of the capillary tube at the boiling point. Care should be taken to avoid breathing fumes of carbon tetrachloride, and methanol which is flammable should not be near an exposed flame.

EXPERIMENT TO SHOW DISTILLATION

This process may be used to obtain a pure liquid from one which has dissolved or suspended materials in it. Example: put a solution of bluestone (copper sulphate) in the flask and add some mud. When the flask is heated the liquid boils about 100°C and water vapor or steam passes over into the condenser. There the cooling effect of water circulating through the condenser jacket makes water vapor condense to pure water in the inner tube.

If impurities in the water are readily vaporized (volatile) they will be carried over with the water vapor. Non-volatile materials such as bluestone or clay remain in the distilling flask.

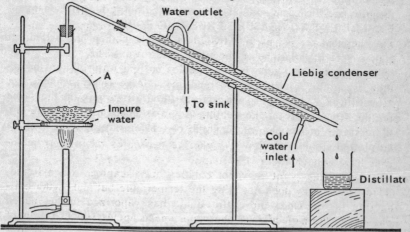

EXPERIMENT TO SHOW SUBLIMATION

Set up a beaker of some naphthalene flakes or benzoic acid crystals over low heat. Place a cut out cardboard ring on the rim of the beaker and a filter paper. Support an inverted beaker on the ring. The temperature should be low enough to prevent the crystals melting. After an hour or more, crystals formed by sublimation are seen growing from the filter paper, and in the upper beaker.

MOLECULAR MOTIONS AND TEMPERATURE

At any temperature in a solid, liquid or gas the particles are moving. The different types of possible motion are vibrations, or oscillations, rotations of molecules, and motion in straight lines through space (translationary motion).

Absolute Zero. There is a minimum possible temperature called absolute zero or $0°$ Kelvin ($0°K$). It is $-273°C$ and a substance would have its particles in the lowest possible energy state at this temperature but not at rest.

At any temperature above absolute zero, particles increase their energies of vibration, rotation, or translation. If a solid is heated enough the forces of vibration begin to equal the forces of cohesion and the regular crystal structure breaks down and the solid melts. At this stage there is no rise in temperature. Added heat energy goes toward breaking up the crystal bonding.

Once the solid has melted more added energy makes the temperature of the liquid rise. Example: 80 calories of heat energy are needed to change 1 gram of ice at $0°C$ to 1 gram of water at $0°C$. This is called the heat of fusion of ice. Other solids have their own heats of fusion determined by the strengths of the forces holding the particles together in the regular solid structure.

In a liquid the particles are moving with more energy than in the corresponding solid. As in solids, different particles differ in energy but there is an average energy and most of the particles have energy near the average. Temperature is a measure of the average energy of the particles in a sample of matter.

In the surface layer of a liquid some molecules with above average energy overcome the binding forces and escape as vapor. This explains why sudden evaporation of a liquid such as ether has a rapid cooling effect. Loss of many above energy molecules reduces the average energy or temperature of those remaining. This also explains why evaporation is faster at higher temperatures when more molecules have enough energy to escape.

At the boiling point as vapor bubbles are escaping from a liquid, added heat energy does not raise the temperature but makes the boiling rate faster. Once the entire liquid has vaporized further added heat makes the molecules of the vapor speed up. At $100°C$ 1 gram of water requires about 540 calories of heat energy to change it to 1 gram of steam also at $100°C$.

In a gas added heat energy makes the molecules move faster (increases the translationary energy). The rates of vibration and rotation also increase.

PURE SUBSTANCES AND MIXTURES

Matter is classified chemically as pure substances or mixtures. All pure substances have a definite composition and are either elements or compounds. Mixtures are either solutions or are called mechanical mixtures.

Elements: There are more than 100 elements such as hydrogen, oxygen, iron, gold and so on. Each element has its own distinctive properties because its atoms have the same number of electrons.

Compounds: These are made of two or more elements chemically united in a definite proportion of atoms. Water, common salt, and sucrose (sugar) are common examples of compounds. Water is made of molecules each containing 2 hydrogen atoms for every 1 oxygen atom. Common salt has 1 sodium atom for every 1 chlorine atom.

Solutions: A solution is a homogeneous mixture. It appears to be one substance but has variable composition whereas elements and compounds are also homogeneous but have definite composition. Solutions are discussed in chapter 9, page 69.

Mechanical Mixtures: Some mixtures are made of two or more different kinds of particles. For example, sand examined through a hand lens shows grains of different minerals. Similarly if iron filings are mixed with sulfur powder there are grey iron particles and yellow sulfur grains side by side. Mechanical mixtures are like solutions in having variable composition but are said to be heterogeneous because two or more phases are noticeable.

Phase: Any distinctly uniform sample of matter is said to have one phase. Examples: copper sulfate solution is uniformly blue and consists of one liquid phase. Ice in soda water has one solid phase (ice), one liquid phase (soda water), and one gaseous phase (carbon dioxide bubbles).

Homogeneous samples of matter are elements, compounds, or solutions and have one phase.

Physical Change and Chemical Change: A pure substance has definite physical properties. Example: water boils at $100°C$, freezes at $0°C$, is colorless and odorless, and has a density of 1 g per ml at $4°C$. Physical properties are used to identify a substance. In a physical change a substance does not change its atomic composition but is merely changed in state, or particle size, or temperature. Examples: ice melting to water, steam condensing to water, the tungsten filament glowing white hot in a light bulb.

In chemical changes elements or compounds not present before the change are produced.

Examples of chemical changes are the decomposition of water to hydrogen and oxygen, and the burning of magnesium in air to form magnesium oxide.

CONSTANT COMPOSITION

Elements: An element cannot be broken down to other forms of matter by any chemical process and has a definite composition of one kind of atom.

Compounds: A compound has a definite composition and contains atoms of different elements in a fixed ratio and therefore has a definite composition by weight.

Analysis: A compound is decomposed to its elements and the weight composition is found.

Synthesis: The weight composition of a compound is found by chemically uniting the elements.

EXPERIMENTS TO FIND THE WEIGHT COMPOSITION OF COMPOUNDS

1. An evaporating dish is weighed empty and then weighed again containing some finely powdered bluestone (copper sulfate pentahydrate). The powder is heated gently and stirred constantly until it is all white. The residue is copper sulfate left when the water of the bluestone escapes. After cooling, the dish and contents are weighed. Calculations should show a loss of 36 g of water from 100 g of bluestone.

Other compounds such as potassium chlorate or mercuric oxide may be used. Example: a test tube is weighed, one quarter filled with potassium chlorate and weighed again. The powder is strongly heated and loses oxygen to the air. A solid, potassium chloride remains. This may be weighed to calculate the amount of oxygen in 100 g of potassium chlorate.

2. A synthesis may be done. A weighed sample of finely powdered copper is mixed with several times its bulk of sulfur powder.

When strongly heated the elements react to form a black solid, copper (II) sulfide. Excess sulfur burns away as the gas sulfur dioxide. The solid residue is weighed to find the amount of copper and sulfur in it.

Each compound should show a definite weight composition of elements. Law of Definite Proportions (Constant Composition): A pure compound always contains the same elements in a fixed proportion by weight.

2. ATOMIC STRUCTURE

FUNDAMENTAL PARTICLES

All matter is made of atoms which contain three kinds of fundamental particles: electrons, protons, and neutrons. Each atom has a central core or nucleus containing protons and neutrons packed tightly together and held by nuclear binding forces. The nucleus is about 1/10,000 of the size of the whole atom and contains more than 99% of the mass of the atom. The electrons occupy the space outside of the nucleus.

Mass: Each of these fundamental particles has mass which may be stated in grams:

$$\text{electron mass} = 9.109 \times 10^{-28}\text{g}$$

$$\text{proton mass} = 1.673 \times 10^{-24}\text{g}$$

$$\text{neutron mass} = 1.675 \times 10^{-24}\text{g}$$

In chemistry it is more convenient to use the relative masses of these particles based on the Atomic Mass Unit Scale. One atomic mass unit amu is 1/12 of the mass of the C^{12} atom taken as 12.0000 amu

$$1 \text{ atomic mass unit} = 1.66 \times 10^{-24}\text{g}$$

On this scale the proton has mass 1 amu, and so does the neutron. The electron has mass 1/1836 of the proton's mass and may be ignored in chemical calculations by simply saying that it has zero mass.

Charge: No experiment has ever detected a charge smaller than the negative charge on the electron. Therefore the electron is said to carry unit elementary charge. A proton carries unit positive charge, and the neutron is neutral having no charge.

Quantity of electric charge is measured in coulombs and on this scale

$$1 \text{ electron (elementary charge)} = -1.6 \times 10^{-19} \text{ coul}$$

$$1 \text{ proton (elementary charge)} = +1.6 \times 10^{-19} \text{ coul}$$

also $$1 \text{ coulomb} = 6.242 \times 10^{18} \text{ elem. ch.}$$

Atoms are electrically neutral because the number of proton charges in the nucleus is balanced by the number of electron charges around the nucleus. Examples: every oxygen atom has 8 protons in the nucleus and 8 electrons around the nucleus. Uranium atoms contain 92 protons and 92 electrons.

THE RUTHERFORD ATOM

Many experiments have been tried to probe the structure of the atom. Fast moving alpha particles (helium nuclei) are fired at thin sheets of metal such as gold foil, and the scattering pattern of the alpha particles is analysed. Such experiments led Rutherford to state a nuclear or planetary model of the atom:

(i) the atom is mainly empty space with a central core or nucleus
(ii) the nucleus is positively charged and contains most of the mass of the atom
(iii) electrons with negative charges to balance the nuclear charge orbit the nucleus like planets around the sun

This model helps explain some behaviors of atoms but is not always the best model. For example, it is sometimes useful to regard an electron as a small particle, at other times as a smeared out cloud of negative charge, and again at other times as a condensed wave packet.

Atomic Number: This is the positive charge on the nucleus of an atom, and therefore the number of protons in the nucleus. It is written as a subscript to the symbol of the element, as in $_8O$ and $_{17}Cl$. Oxygen atoms have 8 protons in each nucleus, all chlorine atoms have 17 protons. The symbol Z is often used to represent atomic number. It follows that because atoms are neutral the atomic number also gives the number of electrons in an atom.

Mass Number: This is the sum of the protons and neutrons in the nucleus of an atom, and is written as a superscript, Na^{23}, U^{238}. The mass number is always an integer because it is a sum of a number of particles. It also indicates the mass of an atom on the atomic mass unit scale because both the proton and neutron have mass 1 amu.

Example: Al^{27} has mass 27 amu. The symbol A is often used to represent mass number. These examples show how the neutron number (N) is readily calculated:

1. What is the structure of the $_{92}U^{235}$ atom?

    Z = 92, therefore 92 protons, and 92 electrons

    A = 235, therefore a total of 235 protons and neutrons

    (N) neutron number $235 - 92 = 143$ $N = A - Z$

2. What is the structure of the $_{11}Na^{23}$ atom?

    In this case $_ZX^A = {}_{11}Na^{23}$

    therefore 11 protons, 11 electrons, and $23 - 11 = 12$ neutrons.

In some of the lighter atoms the neutron number equals the proton number but in the heavier atoms such as uranium the ratio of protons to neutrons is about $1 : 1.5$.

Nucleons: This term is used for both the protons and neutrons of a nucleus because they are so alike in properties other than the difference in charge.

Isotopes: All atoms of the same element contain the same nuclear charge and the same number of electrons, and it is the number and arrangement of electrons that determine the chemical properties of an element. Atoms of the same atomic number may differ in neutron number. Isotopes are atoms of the same element differing in mass because of a different number of neutrons. Examples: $_{92}U^{235}$ and $_{92}U^{238}$ are uranium isotopes.

U-235 has 92 protons, 92 electrons, and 235 – 92 = 143 neutrons

U-238 has 92 protons, 92 electrons, and 238 – 92 = 146 neutrons

Atomic Weight: Most elements occur in nature as mixtures of their isotopes. Examples: natural uranium contains U-235 and U-238 atoms, and all chlorine compounds contain Cl-35 and Cl-37 isotopes.

The atomic weight of an element is the average of the weights of the naturally occurring isotopes taking account of their relative abundance. Example: there are approximately 3 Cl-35 atoms for every 1 Cl-37 atom in any natural sample of chlorine or its compounds.

$$\text{Atomic Weight} = \frac{\text{total weight of sample}}{\text{number of atoms in sample}}$$

$$= \frac{(3 \times 35) + (1 \times 37)}{4} = 35.5 \text{ amu}$$

It is possible to calculate the natural ratio of isotopes if the atomic weight is known. Example: boron has AW of 10.8 and is a mixture of the isotopes B^{10} and B^{11}. If there are n atoms of B^{11} for every 1 B^{10} atom, then

$$\text{AW(10.8)} = \frac{\text{total weight of sample}}{\text{number of atoms in sample}} = \frac{(1 \times 10) + (n \times 11)}{n + 1}$$

therefore 10.8 (n + 1) = 10 + 11n, or 0.2n = 0.8

$$n = 4$$

There are 4 B^{11} atoms for every 1 B^{10} atom.

Note that the atomic weight need not be an integer but is close in value to the mass numbers.

Atomic Mass Unit Scale: Both atomic weights and mass numbers are based on the scale in which the mass of the C-12 atom is taken as 12.0000 amu. Atomic weights are taken in detail in chapter 8, page 55.

RADIOACTIVITY

Some of the heavier elements such as radium and uranium break down to form smaller atoms by ejecting particles and radiation from their nuclei. This is a spontaneous process by which a relatively unstable ratio of protons to neutrons in the nucleus changes to a more favorable ratio.

Three types of radiation are commonly emitted: alpha particles, beta particles, and gamma radiation.

Alpha Particles: An alpha particle is a high speed helium nucleus and therefore consists of two protons bound to two neutrons. The alpha particle thus carries a charge of +2 elementary charges, and travels only a short distance in air before losing most of its energy in collision with gas molecules. The helium nucleus readily picks up two electrons at this time to become an ordinary helium atom. The Greek letter (α) alpha is often used to denote an alpha particle, but it is also represented by He^{2+} or $_2He^4$.

Alpha Emission:

$$_{92}U^{238} \longrightarrow _{90}Th^{234} + _2He^4$$

The new atom formed has mass number 4 amu less than before and atomic number 2 units less. Therefore alpha decay yields an element two steps down the periodic table. Note that mass and charge are conserved: $238 = 234 + 4$, and $92 = 90 + 2$

The outer valence electron number readily adjusts to that of the new element formed. If it is unstable also, a series of decays occurs until a stable non-radioactive atom such as lead is formed.

Beta Emission: A beta particle is a high speed electron. It may be traveling with more than 90% of the speed of light. The particle is lost by a nucleus in which a neutron changes to form a proton, an electron and an unusual particle called an anti-neutrino.

neutron $\longrightarrow$ proton + beta particle + anti-neutrino

$$_0n^1 \longrightarrow _1H^1 + _{-1}e^0 + \bar{\nu}$$

The proton remains in the nucleus thus making a new atom with nuclear charge one more than the previous atom. The element formed is therefore one place ahead in the table of the elements.

Again it is easy for outer electron number to adjust to give a neutral atom

$$_{90}Th^{234} \longrightarrow _{91}Pa^{234} + _{-1}e^0 \text{ (beta particle)}$$

The Greek letter (β) beta is sometimes used to represent the beta particle. The particle soon slows down by collision in air to become a stray electron.

Note again that in beta emission, mass number and charge number are conserved: $234 = 234 + 0$, and $90 = 91 - 1$

Gamma Radiation: This is a form of high energy electromagnetic radiation like light. Gamma rays resemble X rays, but have more energy. Loss of gamma rays makes a nucleus settle down in energy. The Greek Letter (γ) gamma is often used to represent this type of radiation.

NUCLEAR FISSION

A nucleus such as U-235 or Pu-239 may absorb a neutron ejected by another nucleus and split to form two lighter nuclei, 1 to 3 free neutrons, and radiant energy.

$$_{92}U^{235} + {}_0n^1 \longrightarrow {}_{56}Ba^{139} + {}_{36}Kr^{94} + 3{}_0n^1 + \text{Energy}$$

The lighter atoms need not be barium and krypton, but may be a pair with similar masses. This splitting of the nucleus to two nuclei is nuclear fission.

Chain Reaction: The free neutrons emitted during nuclear fission may be absorbed by other U-235 nuclei and in turn produce more free neutrons. This may build up to an uncontrollable rate as a chain reaction in a millionth of a second. Large amounts of energy are set free in accordance with the law of conservation of mass-energy.

Einstein's Mass-Energy Equation: In a nuclear reaction, some matter is converted to free energy and the equation $E = mc^2$, derived by Einstein, applies. E is the energy liberated (in joules), m is the mass in kilograms of matter converted to energy, and c is the speed of light 3×10^8 m/sec. The very large factor c^2 indicates that conversion of a relatively small mass releases a large amount of energy. This is what makes nuclear reactions such an important source of energy.

Critical Mass: In a lump of uranium some neutrons escape through the surface while others are striking uranium nuclei and causing fission and the release of more neutrons. An uncontrollable chain reaction will not occur if the number escaping is relatively large. As the size of the piece of uranium is increased, relatively fewer free neutrons escape and more cause fission inside the metal. The critical mass is the size of a piece of uranium in which a self-sustaining chain reaction rapidly builds up to a nuclear explosion. Therefore a uranium bomb must have at least the critical mass of uranium as one piece.

Nuclear Fusion: Two deuterium (heavy hydrogen) nuclei may fuse or join to form a helium nucleus and in the process matter is converted to large amounts of energy. There is no minimum critical mass of deuterium to cause fusion, but the temperature must be of the order of 10^{10} °K. This condition is obtained by exploding a uranium fission bomb near the deuterium. Then for a brief time the temperature is high enough to start the fusion which increases rapidly.

Half Life: The half life of a radioactive isotope is the time in which half of the atoms of the isotope will have decayed to some other isotope. Example: radioactive Na^{24} has a half life of 14.8 hours. If we start with 100 g of the species now, there will be 50 g remaining after 14.8 hours, and the sample will contain Na^{23} stable atoms from those that decayed. After a further 14.8 hours there will be 25 g of Na^{24} remaining and so on. After 10 half life periods (148 hours) about 0.09 g of the Na^{24} would remain and the rest of the sample would be sodium-23.

3. ELECTRON ARRANGEMENTS

The Rutherford planetary model of the atom was altered to explain why only certain wavelengths of light are absorbed or emitted by atoms. Bohr suggested that the electrons were restricted to some definite paths instead of being able to orbit any distance from the nucleus. When an electron absorbs just the right amount of energy as light it jumps to another permitted orbit farther from the nucleus. Similarly an electron might drop from a higher energy to an empty orbital path closer to the nucleus and give out the extra energy as light or other electromagnetic radiation.

Electron Shells: The layers around the nucleus in which the electrons occur are called electron shells and they are numbered or lettered

shell number	1	2	3	4 etc.,
letter	K	L	M	N etc.,

The 1st or K shell is closest to the nucleus and electrons fill the shells of lower energy first. There is a maximum capacity rule. No shell may hold more electrons than 2 x (number of the shell)^2. Examples: the 1st shell may hold 2 x 1^2 = 2 electrons, the 2nd shell 2 x 2^2 = 8 electrons, the 5th shell 2 x 5^2 = 50 electrons.

The shells fill up in order from element number 1, hydrogen to element number 18, argon, then for the remaining elements the order of filling is irregular.

The electron shell arrangement for the first twenty elements is shown in the table:

Atomic Number(Z)	Element	Symbol	K	L	M	N
1	Hydrogen	H	1			
2	Helium	He	2	shell complete		
3	Lithium	Li	2	1		
4	Beryllium	Be	2	2		
5	Boron	B	2	3		
6	Carbon	C	2	4		
7	Nitrogen	N	2	5		
8	Oxygen	O	2	6		
9	Fluorine	F	2	7		
10	Neon	Ne	2	8	two complete shells	

11	Sodium	Na	2	8	1	
12	Magnesium	Mg	2	8	2	
13	Aluminum	Al	2	8	3	
14	Silicon	Si	2	8	4	
15	Phosphorus	P	2	8	5	
16	Sulfur	S	2	8	6	
17	Chlorine	Cl	2	8	7	
18	Argon	Ar	2	8	8	
19	Potassium	K	2	8	8	1
20	Calcium	Ca	2	8	8	2

After a stable octet is filled at argon, element 18, the 19th electron goes into the N shell although the M shell has a possible capacity of 18 electrons. The 20th electron also goes to the N shell. Starting with element 21, scandium, the M shell begins to fill up in an irregular way.

Stability of the Inert Gases: The noble gas family of helium, neon, argon, krypton, xenon, and radon shows a particular lack of chemical activity and until recently no one had ever succeeded in making a compound of any member of this family. The table shows that helium has a complete shell of 2 electrons, and that the other noble gases have 8 electrons in the outermost shell. Therefore an outer layer of 8 electrons must have a particular stability and for this reason, a group of 8 outer electrons in an atom is called a stable octet.

The chemical activity of all other elements involves the transfer or sharing of electrons to make atoms have a stable outer octet.

Electron Dot Formulas: The electron arrangements of atoms may be shown as in these examples:

	K	L	M	N		
oxygen	2	6			electron dot form	$:\overset{..}{\underset{..}{O}}:$
chlorine	2	8	7		electron dot form	$:\overset{..}{\underset{..}{Cl}}:$
potassium	2	8	8	1	electron dot form	$K\cdot$

The inner complete shells or octets are not shown in the dot formulas, but only the outer electrons involved in forming chemical bonds.

Ionization Energy, Electron Affinity, Electronegativity: These are different measures of the attraction which an atom has for its outer shell electrons.

The ionization energy is the energy absorbed by an atom to remove one outer electron from the attractive force of the nucleus to such a distance that the electron may be considered to be no longer attracted. Elements with a low ionization energy (ionization potential) readily lose electrons and are therefore chemically active. Most metals are examples.

The chemically inactive noble gas elements have high ionization potentials.

Electron affinity is the energy released when an atom gains an electron to form a negatively charged ion(anion). The nonmetals of the fluorine family are chemically active and show high electron affinities.

The electronegativity of an element is derived from measures of ionization energy, electron affinity, and other properties. It may be defined as the measure of the attraction of an atom for the shared electron pair which holds the atom bonded to another. A chemical bond is simply any force of electrical attraction between electrons and the positive nuclei of the atoms held together in a sample of matter. Types of bonds are broadly classified as

(i) covalent . (ii) ionic (iii) metallic

although intermediate types occur.

The Electronegativities of Elements in the Periodic Table

2.1 H																	He
1.0 Li	1.5 Be											2.0 B	2.5 C	3.0 N	3.5 O	4.0 F	Ne
0.9 Na	1.2 Mg											1.5 Al	1.8 Si	2.1 P	2.5 S	3.0 Cl	Ar
0.8 K	1.0 Ca	1.3 Sc	1.5 Ti	1.6 V	1.6 Cr	1.5 Mn	1.8 Fe	1.8 Co	1.8 Ni	1.9 Cu	1.6 Zn	1.6 Ga	1.8 Ge	2.0 As	2.4 Se	2.8 Br	Kr
0.8 Rb	1.0 Sr	1.2 Y	1.4 Zr	1.6 Nb	1.8 Mo	1.9 Tc	2.2 Ru	2.2 Rh	2.2 Pd	1.9 Ag	1.7 Cd	1.7 In	1.8 Sn	1.9 Sb	2.1 Te	2.5 I	Xe
0.7 Cs	0.9 Ba	1.2 Lu	1.3 Hf	1.5 Ta	1.7 W	1.9 Re	2.2 Os	2.2 Ir	2.2 Pt	2.4 Au	1.9 Hg	1.8 Tl	1.8 Pb	1.9 Bi	2.0 Po	2.2 At	Rn
0.8 Fr	0.9 Ra																

COVALENCE

Atoms with the same or slightly different electronegativities may form molecules by sharing pairs of electrons. This is covalent bonding. The shared electrons hold the two atoms together. A molecule is a definite unit of matter composed of atoms with relatively strong covalent bonds between them. In comparison, the forces of attraction between neighboring molecules are relatively weak and are called Van der Waal's forces.

Certain nonmetallic elements occur as gases at room temperature and pressure, and are composed of diatomic molecules in which two atoms are covalently bonded. Examples are hydrogen H_2, oxygen O_2, nitrogen N_2, fluorine F_2, and chlorine Cl_2.

Hydrogen Molecule: A hydrogen atom has only one electron. Two hydrogen atoms form a covalent bond by sharing one electron each in such a way that the electrons may be considered to be mainly located between the two nuclei. The electron dot diagram is

$$H \cdot + \cdot H \longrightarrow H:H \qquad H-H$$

A chlorine atom with 2, 8, 7 electrons is 1 short of an outer stable octet. Two chlorine atoms share a pair of electrons in the chlorine molecule. The formation of the fluorine molecule F_2 may be shown similarly because the F atom also has 7 electrons in the outer shell.

$$:\ddot{C}l \cdot + \cdot \ddot{C}l: \longrightarrow :\ddot{C}l : \ddot{C}l: \qquad Cl-Cl$$

In oxygen there are 6 electrons in the outer shell, and 2 are needed to complete the shell. Two O atoms share 4 electrons (2 pairs).

$$:\ddot{O}: + :\ddot{O}: \longrightarrow :\ddot{O}::\ddot{O}: \qquad O=O \quad Double \ bond$$

Nitrogen atoms are 3 electrons short in the L shell, therefore

$$:N: + :N: \longrightarrow :N::N: \qquad N \equiv N \ triple \ bond$$

Bar (Graphic) Formulas: A shared pair of electrons is called a single covalent bond and may be represented by a line drawn between the two atoms sharing the pair. It is understood that each atom on the end of the bond contributes one electron to the pair. A double covalent bond is two shared electron pairs between two atoms, and a triple covalent bond is three shared electron pairs between two atoms. Thus the H_2 molecule has the structural formula H–H, O_2 is O = O, N_2 is N ≡ N, Cl_2 is Cl – Cl, F_2 is F– F.

In these examples the atoms sharing the electrons are identical and the covalent bond is said to be non-polar.

Covalent Bonds Between Different Atoms (Polar Covalence): If different atoms share electrons and the atoms differ in electronegativity the bond is classed as polar covalent. The difference in electronegativity is slight and the electron pair is not equally shared but drawn closer to the more electronegative atom. Examples: the gas hydrogen chloride has the shared pair drawn closer to the more electronegative Cl atom. This atom acquires a slight excess negative charge shown in the diagram by δ^- (delta negative). At the same time the H atom is made slightly positive and is shown with a δ^+ charge

$$\begin{array}{cc} H & :\ddot{C}l: \\ \delta^+ & \delta^- \end{array}$$

If the electronegativities of hydrogen, chlorine, and fluorine are noted in the table (page 19) it is seen that F being more electronegative than Cl should form a more polar covalent bond with hydrogen.

Other Examples:

The oxygen to hydrogen bonds in water are polar covalent because the O atom is more electronegative. There is also evidence that the water molecule is not a straight line molecule but is bent and has an angle of about 105° between the two O-H bonds. This greatly affects the physical properties of water and ice and is discussed further on pages 25 and 66.

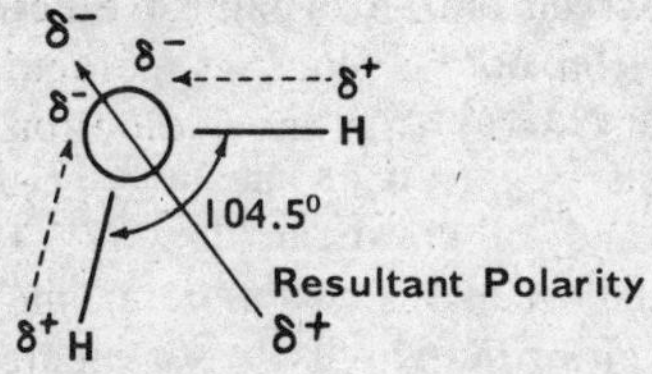

Fig. 3-1

A carbon atom has 4 electrons in the outer shell and forms 4 single covalent bonds to 4 H atoms in methane

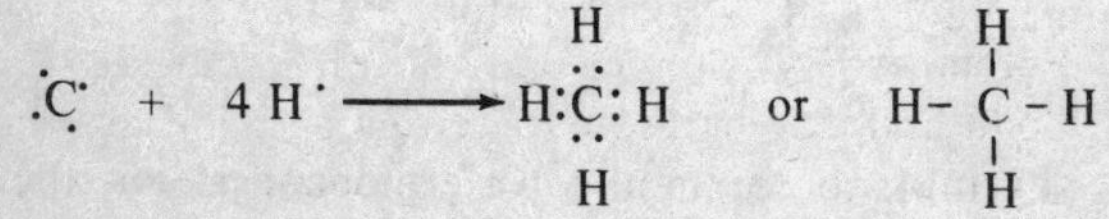

$$.\overset{\cdot}{\underset{\cdot}{C}}\cdot \ + \ 4\,H\cdot \ \longrightarrow \ H:\overset{\cdot\cdot}{\underset{\cdot\cdot}{C}}:H \quad \text{or} \quad H-\overset{\displaystyle H}{\underset{\displaystyle H}{C}}-H$$

Carbon tetrachloride has a similar structural formula.

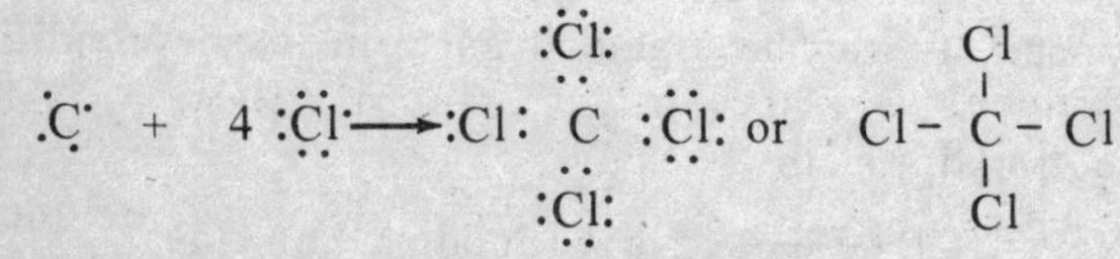

$$.\overset{\cdot}{\underset{\cdot}{C}}\cdot \ + \ 4 :\overset{\cdot\cdot}{\underset{\cdot\cdot}{Cl}}\!-\!\longrightarrow :\overset{\cdot\cdot}{Cl}: \ C \ :\overset{\cdot\cdot}{\underset{\cdot\cdot}{Cl}}: \quad \text{or} \quad Cl-\overset{\displaystyle Cl}{\underset{\displaystyle Cl}{C}}-Cl$$

Chloroform has the bar structural formula

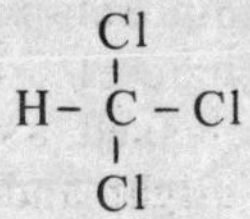

$$H-\overset{\displaystyle Cl}{\underset{\displaystyle Cl}{C}}-Cl$$

In these examples each C-H or C-Cl bond is polar covalent. If the four atoms are symmetrical around the central carbon the polarities cancel out and the molecule is nonpolar as in the case of CH_4 and CCl_4. Chloroform $CHCl_3$ is not symmetrical and therefore polar.

Ammonia has a N atom with 5 outer electrons and requires 3 for a complete octet. Therefore 3 H atoms unite to 1 N.

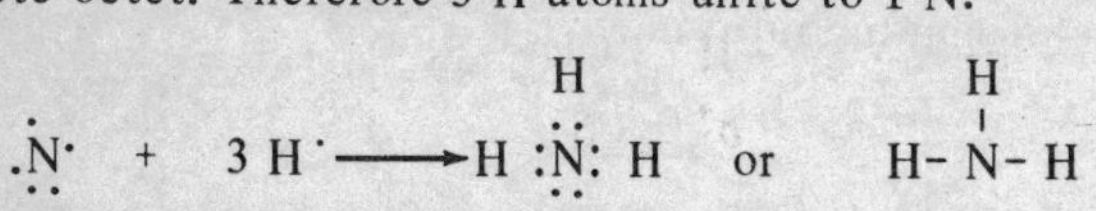

$$.\overset{\cdot}{\underset{\cdot\cdot}{N}}\cdot \ + \ 3\,H\cdot \ \longrightarrow \ H:\overset{\cdot\cdot}{N}:H \quad \text{or} \quad H-\overset{\displaystyle H}{N}-H$$

The molecule is polar and the unshared electron pair on the N atom contributes to the polarity.

Covalence: The covalence of an atom is the number of shared electrons it uses in covalent bonding. Examples: in water an oxygen atom shares two electrons with hydrogen, and each hydrogen shares 1 electron with oxygen. The covalence of oxygen is 2, and of hydrogen 1. Carbon in most of its compounds has its atoms forming 4 covalent bonds with the 4 electrons of its atoms. Therefore its covalence is 4. Covalences are used in writing chemical formulas, chapter 6, page 38.

The covalent bond may be defined as the electrical force of attraction of the shared electron pair localized in space, for the nuclei of the atoms sharing the electrons.

Ionic Bonds and Electrovalence:

In the table of electronegativities on page 19, the metals lithium, sodium, magnesium, and others near the left hand side have low electronegativities and readily combine with nonmetals such as fluorine, oxygen, and chlorine which are at the right on the table and have high electronegativities. The chemical bond is classed as ionic if the electronegativity difference is large. The metal atom may be regarded as almost completely transfering the 1 or 2 electrons of its outer shell to the nonmetal atom.

Examples: sodium Na 2, 8, 1   with chlorine Cl 2, 8, 7

gives sodium ion Na$^+$ 2, 8   with chloride ion Cl$^-$ 2, 8, 8

This exposes a stable octet in the Na$^+$ and completes the outer octet of the Cl$^-$. The ionic (electrovalent) bond is the strong force of electrical attraction between the positive and negative ions of the ionic compound. It may be regarded as the extreme condition of polar bonding.

Using the electron dot method

$$Na \cdot + :\overset{\frown}{\underset{\cdot\cdot}{Cl}}: \longrightarrow Na^+ \, \bar{Cl} \text{ sodium chloride}$$

Similarly with potassium and fluorine

$$K \; 2, 8, 8, 1 + F \; 2, 7 \longrightarrow K^+ \; 2, 8, 8 \quad F^- \; 2, 8$$

or $K \cdot + :\overset{\cdot\cdot}{\underset{\cdot\cdot}{F}}: \longrightarrow K^+F^-$ potassium fluoride

In forming magnesium oxide, the metal atom loses 2 electrons to the 0 atom which is 2 short of an octet.

$$Mg \; 2, 8, 2 + 0 \quad 2, 6 \longrightarrow Mg^{2+} \; 2, 8 \quad 0^{2-} \; 2, 8$$

When magnesium or calcium reacts with fluorine or chlorine, 2 electrons must be lost by the metal atom but the nonmetal needs only 1. Therefore the combining ratio is

$$Ca \; 2, 8, 8, 2 + \begin{matrix} F \; 2, 7 \\ F \; 2, 7 \end{matrix} \longrightarrow Ca^{2+} \; 2, 8, 8 + \begin{matrix} F^- \; 2, 8 \\ F^- \; 2, 8 \end{matrix}$$

or $\quad$ Ca: + 2:$\ddot{\text{F}}$: $\longrightarrow$ Ca^{2+} 2 F$^-$ calcium fluoride

The typical physical properties of ionic compounds are discussed in the next chapter.

Electrovalence: The electrovalence of an atom is the charge on the ion formed when the atom gains or loses electrons in forming an ionic bond.

Examples: sodium has an electrovalence of +1 because its atom has 11 protons and 11 electrons. The atom loses 1 electron and forms the Na$^+$ ion with 11 protons and 10 electrons so that there is a surplus of 1 positive charge. Chlorine has 17 protons and 17 electrons and gains 1 electron to form the Cl$^-$ ion with an electrovalence of −1 equal to the charge on the ion.

Electrovalences are used in writing chemical formulas, chapter 6.

4. CHEMICAL BONDS, STRUCTURE OF MATTER, GEOMETRY OF SOLIDS

ISOLATED ATOMS:

Matter does not usually occur as isolated atoms. The common examples at room temperature are helium, neon and other gases of the noble gas family. They form monatomic gases because the atoms have stable numbers of electrons in the outer shells and do not form molecules. At a high enough temperature a metal may be vaporized to single atoms but this is not a usual state of a sample of matter.

With the exception of non-crystalline or amorphous solids, page 6, others are classed as ionic crystals, covalent crystals, and metallic crystals.

IONIC CRYSTALS:

The repeating structural units in an ionic solid are positive and negative ions held by Coulombic forces of electrostatic attraction. The kind of crystal structure depends on the strength of the forces, the sizes of the ions and the ratio of positive to negative ions in the particular compound.

Sodium chloride contains 1 Na^+ ion for every 1 Cl^- arranged with 6 Cl^- around each Na^+, and 6 Na^+ around each Cl^-. In calcium chloride there are $2Cl^-$ for every 1 Ca^{2+} ion. No ion is attached in particular to one other. Therefore the term molecule is not used for ionic compounds. The formula NaCl or Na^+Cl^- merely indicates the ratio of the ions in the solid. The structure of NaCl is shown on page 25. Ionic bonds are strong enough to make these crystals hard and have high melting points. When deformed by strong forces the crystals break up. This brittleness may be explained by strong repulsion between ions of the same charge when brought together in the deformed layers.

Ionic solids are not conductors of electricity because the ions are vibrating only in the solid. However when melted the ion lattice breaks down and the molten substance conducts current by a directed flow of the ions.

Liquids such as water with polar molecules will dissolve ionic solids if they can overcome the attractive forces between the ions. Nonpolar liquids such as benzene do not dissolve ionic solids such as sodium chloride.

MOLECULAR COVALENT SOLIDS:

The pairs of electrons in the covalent bonds of a molecular crystal are mainly confined between the bonded atoms and there is little interaction between neighboring molecules. The relatively weak forces of attraction in molecular solids such as iodine and naphthalene crystals are called van der Waal's forces. Typically the solids have low melting points and may sublime at room temperature to form individual covalent molecules in the vapor phase. They are non-conductors of electricity and dissolve in nonpolar solvents.

ICE:

This is an example of a solid with polar covalent bonding and hydrogen bonding. The small electronegative oxygen atoms draw the shared electrons closer so that the hydrogens have extra positive charge. Neighboring oxygen atoms attract the nearby hydrogens with a force strong enough to be classed as a definite bond. It is called the hydrogen bond.

NETWORK SOLIDS:

Diamond, quartz (silicon dioxide), and silicon carbide SiC are examples of covalent or polar covalent solids in which equally strong bonds extend in definite directions from atom to atom through the entire crystal. The molecule is simply the whole crystal. Because of the many strong covalent bonds network solids are very hard and have high melting points.

For the same reason they are insoluble in polar or nonpolar solvents.

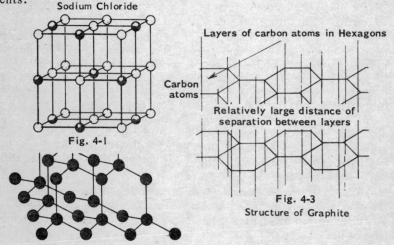

Sodium Chloride

Fig. 4-1

Layers of carbon atoms in Hexagons

Carbon atoms

Relatively large distance of separation between layers

Fig. 4-3
Structure of Graphite

Fig. 4-2   Structure of diamond.

In diamond each carbon atom has 4 electrons in the outer shell forming 4 single covalent bonds to 4 other carbon atoms arranged tetrahedrally. Quartz, SiO_2 is common in sand. Silicon carbide is the hard grinding material carborundum.

Graphite is a layer type of solid. There are strong covalent bonds between the hexagonally arranged carbon atoms in the sheet. Relatively weak forces between the layers allow them to slide easily. This makes graphite greasy to touch and a useful dry lubricant.

METALLIC SOLIDS:

Most metal atoms have 1 or 2 electrons in the outer shell. Aluminum has 3, and tin and lead have 4. The inner layers of electrons are held by relatively strong forces from the nuclei but the outer electrons may readily wander from one atom to another because many empty electron orbitals are available. A metal may be pictured as a regular arrangement of positive ions held in place by the attractive forces of the outer mobile electrons. The metallic bond is a special type of covalent bond which gives metals characteristic properties.

Metals usually have high density because the atoms are closely packed. They are good conductors of electricity because the outer loosely held electrons may readily drift in a directed flow through the metal and thus form an electric current. Metals are good heat conductors because added heat energy becomes kinetic energy of the electrons which readily drift through the solid and carry the energy along.

Metals are malleable, they may be hammered into sheets, and are ductile, they may be drawn out as wires. This is because strong repulsive forces are not set up between the positive ions if layers slide over one another. When the various wavelengths of light strike a metal surface the light energy interacts in such a way with the outer electrons of the metal that most light is reflected. This makes metals opaque to light and causes the particular metallic shine or luster common to most metals.

CRYSTAL GEOMETRY

METALLIC CRYSTALS

Metal atoms are very closely packed in the solid. The atoms may be regarded as spheres of the same size and the close packing relates to the possible ways in which spheres of the same size may be arranged in layers in contact. There are three principal metal structures shown in the diagrams.

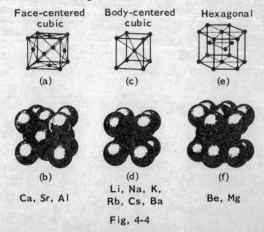

Fig. 4-4

In (a) and (e) each atom has co-ordination number 12, indicating that the atom is in contact with 12 other atoms. This is the maximum packing of similar spheres. In (c) the co-ordination number is 8, and the packing is not quite as close. The external crystal form of a metal is determined by the packing of the atoms.

Ionic Solids: The number of nearest neighbors or co-ordination number is influenced by the formula of the ionic compound and the relative sizes of the positive and negative ions.

Examples: sodium chloride has 1 Na^+ for every 1 Cl^- and as the metal ion is about half the size of the Cl^-, the co-ordination number is only 6. Caesium chloride CsCl also has 1 Cs^+ ion for every 1 Cl^- but the metal ion is closer in radius to the Cl^- and this allows a closer packing and co-ordination number of 8.

Na^+ radius 0.95 A, Cs^+ radius 1.69 A, Cl^- radius 1.81 A. Calcium fluoride has 1 Ca^{2+} for every 2 F^- and the close packing in this solid differs because of the ion ratio as well as ion sizes.

Covalent Crystals: In a network solid such as diamond the crystal structure is a result of the strongly directed four covalent bonds from each carbon to four other carbons arranged in a tetrahedral pattern as in diagram 4-2, page 25.

In other molecular crystals the individual molecules are oriented in directions which depend on the shape and size of the molecules and the strengths of the van der Waal's forces.

5. THE GAS LAWS

PRESSURE OF A GAS: The molecules of a gas are always moving and exert pressure when they collide with any surface. Therefore, air has a pressure and it is measured by the simple mercury barometer of diagram A. Standard air pressure supports a column of mercury 760 mm high. Standard pressure is also called 1 atmosphere (1 atm).

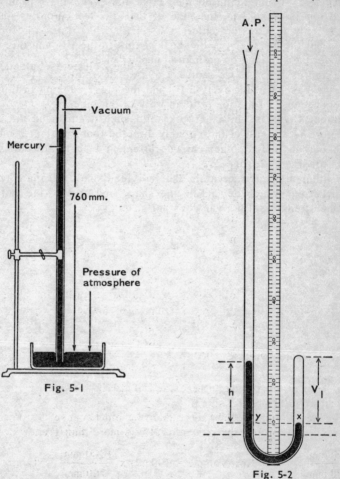

Fig. 5-1

Fig. 5-2

In diagram B, the enclosed sample of gas exerts pressure on the mercury surface at X. This equals the pressure at point Y horizontally opposite. If this were not so the mercury would move until the pressures were equal. The enclosed gas has pressure equal to air pressure plus the pressure of the mercury column of length h cm.

EXPERIMENT TO SHOW BOYLE'S LAW

Use the apparatus of diagram B. Measure the length of the trapped air column. This is a measure of the volume of the gas if the tube has uniform internal diameter. Next measure h in cm and add the atmospheric pressure measured in cm of mercury. This is the pressure of the gas. More mercury may be added to the open tube so that the enclosed gas is compressed and new pressure and volume readings are taken. This is repeated for other readings. The temperature may be assumed constant during the experiment, and the gas has fixed mass because molecules cannot enter or leave the enclosed sample.

The readings show that as pressure increases the volume of gas decreases, or volume varies inversely as pressure.

That is, if the pressure is doubled the volume is halved. If the pressure is made ten times as great, the volume becomes one tenth of its previous size. This is Boyle's Law: the volume of a fixed mass of gas at constant temperature varies inversely as the pressure. The law may be stated P x V = constant, or

$$P_1 \text{ x } V_1 = P_2 + V_2 = \ldots\ldots$$

BOYLE'S LAW PROBLEMS

1. A gas at standard pressure has a volume of 5.0 liters. What is its volume at a pressure of 9.2 atmospheres?

$$V_1 = 5.0 \text{ liters} \qquad\qquad V_2 = ? \quad \text{liters}$$
$$P_1 = 1 \text{ atm} \xrightarrow{\text{increases}} P_2 = 9.2 \text{ atm}$$
$$V_1 \text{ x } P_1 = V_2 \text{ x } P_2, \text{ or } V_2 = V_1 \text{ x } \frac{P_1}{P_2}$$

the new volume = old volume x a pressure ratio. In this problem the pressure ratio must be less than 1, because increased pressure makes the new volume less than the old.

$$\text{new volume} = 5.0 \text{ liters x } \frac{1 \text{ atm}}{9.2 \text{ atm}} = 0.55 \text{ liters}$$

2. What is the volume of a gas at 700 mm Hg pressure if it occupies 300 ml at 1200 mm pressure?

The new volume will be more than the old because the pressure is decreased. Therefore the pressure ratio is more than 1, and is

$$\frac{1200 \text{ mm}}{700 \text{ mm}} \qquad \text{New volume} = 300 \text{ ml x } \frac{1200 \text{ mm}}{700 \text{ mm}} = 514 \text{ ml}$$

Gas Volume and Temperature: When gases are heated their molecules acquire more kinetic energy and speed up. They exert more pressure and if the container walls are elastic the gas will expand to occupy a bigger volume.

EXPERIMENT TO SHOW CHARLES' LAW.

The glass tube contains a fixed mass of gas and it has a constant pressure equal to the air pressure plus the pressure of the small mercury thread. First note the length of the air column when it is not changing and take the temperature of the water bath. This is also the temperature of the trapped air. The tube has uniform internal diameter so that the length is a measure of the volume of the trapped gas. Raise the water temperature about 10°C and after the mercury thread stops moving, again note the length of the air column and the temperature. Take several sets of readings. If the volume of the gas is plotted against temperature, a straight line graph is obtained as in the second diagram.

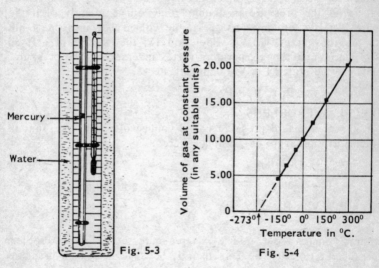

Fig. 5-3   Fig. 5-4

If the lower end of the graph is extended it crosses the x-axis close to -273°C. This corresponds to the gas having zero volume at that temperature. In fact, the gas would liquefy before this temperature was reached. -273°C is the absolute zero of temperature and is called 0° Absolute (0°A) or 0° Kelvin (0°K). The linear relationship is that the volume of a gas varies directly as the temperature in degrees Kelvin.

Celsius (Centigrade) temperature are converted to Kelvin by adding 273.

Examples: 20°C = 20 + 273 = 293°K   -40°C = -40 + 273 = 233°K
Kelvin temperatures are converted to Celsius by subtracting 273.
Examples: 1860°K = 1860 - 273 = 1587°C
              150°K = 150 - 273 = -123°C

Charles' Law: a fixed mass of gas at constant pressure has a volume which varies directly as the absolute temperature. For example, a gas has a volume of 200 ml at 40°C (313°K). Its volume is doubled to 400 ml at 626°K (353°C).

The law may be stated $\dfrac{V}{T^\circ K}$ = constant

or $\dfrac{V_1}{T_1} = \dfrac{V_2}{T_2} = \ldots\ldots\ldots$

CHARLES' LAW PROBLEMS

1. What is the volume of a gas at 200°C if it occupies 10 liters at standard temperature?
Standard temperature is 0°C or 273°K.

$$V_1 = 10 \text{ liters} \qquad\qquad V_2 = ? \text{ liters}$$
$$T_1 = 0^\circ C\ (273^\circ K) \xrightarrow{\text{increases}} T_2 = 200^\circ C\ (473^\circ K)$$

The temperature increase will make the gas expand to a bigger volume, and the relationship may be stated

new volume = old volume x temperature ratio ($^\circ$K)

The temperature ratio must be greater than 1, $\dfrac{473}{273}$ to make the new volume greater.

$$\text{new volume} = 10 \text{ liters x } \frac{473^\circ K}{273^\circ K} = 17.4 \text{ liters}$$

2. What is the volume of a gas at -15°C if it is 60 ml at 30°C?

$$V_1 = 60 \text{ ml} \qquad\qquad V_2 = ? \text{ ml}$$
$$T_1 = 30^\circ C\ (303^\circ K) \xrightarrow{\text{decreases}} T_2 = 15^\circ C\ (258^\circ K)$$

The temperature decreases and the volume will decrease in the same ratio $\dfrac{258}{303}$

$$\text{new volume} = 60 \text{ ml x } \frac{258^\circ K}{303^\circ K} = 51.1 \text{ ml}$$

VOLUME OF A GAS AFTER PRESSURE AND TEMPERATURE CHANGE

A gas may be collected and its volume, pressure, and temperature noted at room conditions. It is sometimes necessary to find the new volume at a different temperature and pressure. The relationship is
new volume = old volume x pressure ratio x temperature ratio.

Example: a gas has a volume of 480 ml at 25°C and a pressure of 730 mm Hg. What is the volume at STP?
STP is standard temperature (0°C) and standard pressure (760 mm Hg)

$$V_1 = 480 \text{ ml} \qquad\qquad V_2 = ? \text{ ml}$$

$$P_1 = 730 \text{ mm} \xrightarrow[\text{decreases}]{\text{increases}} P_2 = 760 \text{ mm}$$

$$T_1 = 25°C\ (298°K) \longrightarrow T_2 = 0°C\ (273°K)$$

Increased pressure makes the volume less and the pressure ratio is $\dfrac{730.}{760}$. Also, decreased temperature makes the volume less and the temperature ratio is $\dfrac{273}{298}$.

$$\text{new volume} = 480 \text{ ml} \ \text{x} \ \frac{730 \text{ mm}}{760 \text{ mm}} \ \text{x} \ \frac{273°K}{298°K} = 422 \text{ ml}$$

GAS DENSITY

The atoms in solids and liquids are closely packed and the densities are stated in grams per milliliter. Examples: density of water 1 g/ml, density of iron 7.9 g/ml. The average spaces between gas molecules are many times the sizes of the molecules. Therefore gas densities are stated in grams per liter.

$$1 \text{ liter} = 1000 \text{ milliliters}$$

Examples: the density of oxygen at STP = 1.43 g/liter, chlorine has density = 3.2 g/l at STP.

Changes in temperature and pressure may greatly change the volume and therefore the density of a gas. The temperature and pressure of the gas are therefore stated with its density.

Problem: At 120°C and a pressure of 800 mm Hg, 300 ml of a gas weighs 0.78 g. Calculate its density in grams per liter at STP.

(a) Convert the gas volume to STP. The number of molecules in the gas will not change. Therefore the mass of the gas is the same.

$$V_1 = 300 \text{ ml} \qquad\qquad V_2 = ? \text{ ml}$$

$$P_1 = 800 \text{ mm} \xrightarrow[\text{decreases}]{\text{decreases}} P_2 = 760 \text{ mm}$$

$$T_1 = 120°C\ (393°K) \longrightarrow T_2 = 0°C\ (273°K)$$

$$\text{new volume} = 300 \text{ ml} \ \text{x} \ \frac{800 \text{ mm}}{760 \text{ mm}} \ \text{x} \ \frac{273°K}{393°K} = 219 \text{ ml}$$

(b) Density in grams per liter $= \dfrac{\text{Mass (g)}}{\text{Volume (l)}}$

volume of gas = 219 ml = 0.219 liters (1 ml $= \dfrac{1}{1000}$ liter)

$$\text{density of gas} = \frac{0.78 \text{ g}}{0.219 \text{ l}} = 3.56 \text{ g/l at STP}$$

Note that in part (a), decreased pressure makes the gas volume bigger, and the pressure ratio is more than 1. Decreased temperature makes a gas contract in volume, and the temperature ratio is less than 1.

PARTIAL PRESSURES OF GASES:

In a mixture of gases each exerts its own pressure independently of the others. Dalton's law of partial pressures states that the total pressure of a gas mixture is the sum of the pressures of each gas in the mixture. The experiment of page 57 is an example. The gas is left to come to room temperature and the space becomes saturated with water vapor mixed with the oxygen. The water levels are equal therefore the pressure of the mixture equals atmospheric pressure 750 mm Hg. At room temperature $20°C$, saturated water vapor exerts a pressure of 17.5 mm Hg. The pressure of the oxygen is therefore $750 - 17.5 = 732.5$ mm.

CRITICAL TEMPERATURE AND PRESSURE

Increased pressure on a real gas brings the molecules closer together and the intermolecular forces of attraction help liquefy the gas. If the gas molecules have too high a temperature (too high kinetic energy), pressure along will not liquefy the gas to a recognizable liquid phase. Then the gas is said to be above its critical temperature. The critical temperature of a gas is the highest temperature at which pressure alone will liquefy the gas, and the value of the pressure required is called the critical pressure.

DIFFUSION OF GASES

A gas tends to spread out and uniformly fill any container because of the random motion of its molecules and the lack of c o h e s i v e forces. This may be shown by filling a gas bottle with a colored gas such as chlorine or bromine vapor, and closing the bottle with a glass plate. Then an empty bottle is inverted on top of the first and the plate removed. The colored gas diffuses upward until uniformly spread throughout both bottles. Gaseous diffusion is also noticed if you are near an open bottle of concentrated ammonia solution. The pungent odor of ammonia is soon observed because the molecules rapidly diffuse out of the solution.

At a given temperature gas molecules may have any speed from zero up. There is an average speed v_a for the molecules which depends on the temperature of the gas. Most of the molecules have speeds near the average. A moving particle has kinetic energy $E_k = 1/2 \ mv^2$ where m is the mass and v is the speed. If v_a is the average speed of a molecule in a sample of gas, then the average kinetic energy is $1/2 mv_a^2$.

At the same temperature, different gases have the same average E_k. If the gas molecules have different masses it follows that the average speeds will differ. Example: hydrogen H_2 has mass 2 amu, and chlorine Cl_2 has mass 71 amu

$$E_k \text{ (average) for } H_2 = 1/2 \times 2 \times v_H^2$$
$$E_k \text{ (average) for } Cl_2 = 1/2 \times 71 \times v_{Cl}^2$$

Therefore, $1 \times v_H^2 = 35.5 \times v_{Cl}^2$ where v_H is the average speed of a H_2 molecule, and v_{Cl} is that of the Cl_2 at the same temperature.

$$\frac{v_H^2}{v_{Cl}^2} = \frac{35.5}{1} \text{ or } \frac{\text{average speed of } H_2 \text{ molecule}}{\text{average speed of } Cl_2 \text{ molecule}} = \sqrt{\frac{35.5}{1}} = \frac{6}{1} \text{ approx.}$$

Therefore H_2 molecules diffuse 6 times as fast as Cl_2 molecules at the same temperature. This is Graham's Law of Diffusion: the rates of diffusion of gases at the same temperature varies inversely as the square roots of the masses of their molecules.

Example: What is the relative rate of diffusion of hydrogen and sulfur dioxide gas at the same temperature?

The formula weights are $H_2 = 2$ amu, and $SO_2 = 64$ amu

$$\frac{\text{rate of diffusion of } H_2}{\text{rate of diffusion of } SO_2} = \sqrt{\frac{64}{2}} = \sqrt{\frac{32}{1}} = \frac{5.7}{1}$$

EXPERIMENT TO COMPARE RATES OF DIFFUSION:

Obtain a glass tube about 2 ft. long and 1 in internal diameter. Put the tube horizontally on the bench, and add drops of concentrated ammonia solution in one end, and drops of concentrated hydrochloric acid in the other. Stopper the ends. NH_3 molecules and HCl molecules diffuse toward each other and where they meet a ring of white solid ammonium chloride NH_4Cl forms. The ring forms closer to the HCl end because the lighter NH_3 molecules diffuse faster.

GASES AND KINETIC – MOLECULAR THEORY

The gas laws apply to an ideal monatomic gas but are not exact for gases such as oxygen, chlorine and others in which the molecules attract each other, especially at high pressure when they are close together. Helium, neon, mercury vapor, and sodium vapor may be considered as ideal monatomic gases because their atoms are not united in molecules. Some features of an ideal gas are:

(i) no forces of attraction between the atoms

(ii) average distances between the atoms are many times the atomic diameters

(iii) the atoms move in straight lines (translationary motion) with various speeds.

(iv) gravity has no effect on the motion

(v) after collision atoms rebound with as much energy as they had before (elastic collision)

Ideal Gas Equation: This equation applies to an ideal monatomic gas

$$PV = kNT$$

P is the pressure of the gas, or the average force exerted by the atoms bombarding unit surface area of the container. V is the volume of the gas, and K is a particular constant. N is the number of atoms in the gas sample, and T is the temperature in $^\circ K$. The equation is also applied to non-ideal gases in which atoms are united in molecules. Then N is the number of molecules in the gas. If a gas contains the Avogadro number of molecules, 6.02×10^{23} then the quantity is called 1 mole of gas, and the gas equation may be in the form
$PV = RT$ R replaces Nk and is called the gas constant.

Boyle's law may be derived from the gas equation. If T is constant, and so is the mass of the gas (N molecules), then the right hand side has a constant value, or $P \times V$ is constant.

Charles' law may also be derived. If P is constant, and so is the number of molecules (N) or mass of the gas, then V varies directly as T. To keep equality in the gas equation increasing T increases V.

Avogadro's Law. If two gases have the same volume V, the same pressure P, and the same temperature T, then R is the same for both gases. But $R = kN$, therefore the gases must contain the same number of molecules. This is Avogadro's Law: equal volumes of all gases at the same temperature and pressure contain the same number of molecules. It does not apply strictly to real gases but only to ideal monatomic gases.

For 1 mole of a gas (6.02×10^{23} molecules) at STP ($0^\circ C$, 760 mm Hg) V is 22.4 liters. This volume is called the Gram Molecular Volume of a gas.

Gram Molecular Volume (GMV) is the volume occupied by 1 mole of any gas and is 22.4 liters at STP.

Explanation of Boyle's Law: If a gas is compressed in a cylinder fitted with a movable piston until the volume is halved, and the temperature is kept constant, the same number of molecules moving in half the space with the same average kinetic energy will make twice as many collisions per second with the container walls. Therefore the pressure is doubled when the volume is halved.

Explanation of Charles' Law: Increasing the temperature of a gas increases the average kinetic energy of the molecules and therefore the rate of bombardment on the container walls increases also. To maintain a constant pressure on the walls as the temperature rises, the surface area bombarded must increase. Therefore the volume of the gas must rise with the temperature if the pressure is to remain constant.

Vapor Pressure of a Liquid: At a given temperature in a closed container molecules will escape from a liquid and enter the space above the liquid until the space is saturated. There is an equilibrium when the vapor is saturated. The number of molecules entering the vapor phase equals the number returning to the liquid. The pressure of the molecules in the saturated vapor at that temperature is called the vapor pressure.

If the temperature is raised, so is the average energy of the molecules and more are in the vapor at equilibrium and exert more pressure. That is the vapor pressure increases with temperature.

EXPERIMENT TO SHOW VAPOR PRESSURE OF A LIQUID

Set up a simple mercury barometer as shown in diagram A on page 28. Measure the atmospheric pressure (height of the mercury column). Use a bent tube to inject a small drop of water into the bottom of the barometer tube. The bubble of water rises through the mercury column and vaporizes. Its vapor pressure pushes down the mercury level. If another small drop of water is added, the mercury drops more. This happens until the space above the mercury is saturated. At 20°C the mercury level drops 17.5 mm because this is the saturated vapor pressure of water at this temperature.

Other mercury barometers may be set up to measure the vapor pressures of liquids such as benzene and ether using the same method. At the same temperature different liquids have different vapor pressures.

The effect of temperature on vapor pressure may be shown by surrounding the barometer tube of mercury and saturated water vapor with an outer tube through which water at a constant temperature is circulated.

If water is circulated through the jacket at temperature 30°C, 40°C etc., a series of readings of the saturated water vapor pressure in the barometer tube may be taken, and a vapor pressure curve plotted against temperature.

Vapor Pressure and Boiling Point: With increased temperature and increased vapor pressure a liquid reaches a stage at which it boils. Then its vapor pressure equals the atmospheric pressure.

Examples: at 100°C the boiling point of water, saturated water vapor pressure equals 760 mm Hg. At 78°C benzene boils and its vapor pressure at that temperature is 760 mm Hg.

EXPERIMENT TO SHOW FRACTIONAL DISTILLATION

In a solution of liquids such as water and methanol, each has its own vapor pressure at a given temperature. If the distillation apparatus of page 8 is used and the temperature is gradually raised, the mixture begins to boil about 65°C. The vapor distilling over is almost pure methanol at first but contains some water vapor which is also evaporating at that temperature. Not all of the methanol molecules escape from the liquid at the boiling point of methanol. About 100°C the vapor distilling over is mainly water but contains some methanol as well. The beaker collecting the distillate may be changed at different temperature ranges to obtain a partial separation of the two liquids. If some anhydrous copper sulfate is added to each fraction, the intensity of the blue color produced is a measure of the relative amounts of water in each sample.

6. SYMBOLS, FORMULAS, EQUATIONS

Symbols and Formulas: A symbol represents one atom of an element. **Examples**: sodium Na, chlorine Cl. The symbols of some elements are on page 56.

A formula represents a molecule if the element or compound exists as a definite molecular unit. Examples: oxygen O_2, carbon dioxide CO_2, white phosphorus P_4. In a network solid such as silica SiO_2 there is no separate molecule with 1 Si atom bonded to only 2 O atoms. The formula shows the ratio of atoms in the crystal. Similarly ionic compounds such as calcium fluoride CaF_2 are given a formula which indicates the simple ratio of the ions in the compound 1 Ca^{2+} to 2 F^-.

Chemical formulas are written using the valences shown in the table on page 39. The valence is either the charge on the ion formed when an atom gains or loses electrons or is the number of covalent bonds formed by the atom.

Binary Compounds: These have only two elements in the formula as in magnesium oxide MgO, and carbon tetrachloride CCl_4 and the name of the binary compound is

name of first element + part of name of second + IDE (ending) as in

sodium + chlorine $\longrightarrow$ sodium chloride

Rules: (i) The element of positive valence is written first and the one of negative valence second

    (ii) metals are always positive, therefore first

    (iii) the correct formula is written using the "cross over" rule

Variable Valence: An element with 2 valences such as copper is given the name cuprous for the lower valence +1, and cupric for the higher valence +2. Similarly iron +2 is ferrous, iron +3 is ferric. The -ic ending is for the higher valence.

Therefore cuprous oxide is not the same compound as cupric oxide and the name copper oxide is not used because it does not indicate which of the two is meant.

More modern naming distinguishes the variable valence by using copper (II) and copper (I). The numeral in parenthesis is the valence of the preceding element. Examples: ferric oxide has iron with valence +3, and is also called iron (III) oxide.

The "Cross Over" Rule: Write the valence above each element in a binary compound. Ignore the valence signs. Switch the valence numbers by writing them below and after the other element.

+1	+2	+3	+4	+5
H Hydrogen	Ba Barium	Al Aluminum		
Na Sodium	Mg Magnesium	As Arsenic (III) arsenious		As Arsenic (V) arsenic
K Potassium	Ca Calcium	Sb Antimony (III) antimonous		Sb Antimony (V) antimonic
Ag Silver	Zn Zinc	P Phosphorus (III) phosphorous		P Phosphorus (V) phosphoric
Cu Copper (I) cuprous	Cu Copper (II) cupric	Bi Bismuth (III) bismuthous		Bi Bismuth (V) bismuthic
Hg Mercury (I) mercurous	Hg Mercury (II) mercuric		C Carbon	Si Silicon
	Fe Iron (II) ferrous	Fe Iron (III) ferric		
	Cr Chromium (II) chromous	Cr Chromium (III) chromic		
	Sn Tin (II) stannous		Sn Tin (IV) stannic	

-1	-2
F Fluorine	O Oxygen
Cl Chlorine	S Sulfur (in sulfides)
Br Bromine	
I Iodine	

Examples:

$$\text{sodium chloride is } \overset{1}{Na}\!\!\times\!\!\overset{1}{Cl} \longrightarrow Na_1Cl_1 \text{ written NaCl}$$

$$\text{zinc bromide is } \overset{2}{Zn}\!\!\times\!\!\overset{1}{Br} \longrightarrow Zn_1Br_2 \text{ written } ZnBr_2$$

$$\text{aluminum oxide is } \overset{3}{Al}\!\!\times\!\!\overset{2}{O} \longrightarrow Al_2O_3$$

$$\text{magnesium sulfide is } \overset{2}{Mg}\!\!\times\!\!\overset{2}{S} \longrightarrow Mg_2S_2 \text{ but a 2:2}$$

ratio is simplified to 1:1, therefore MgS

This ratio is not simplified in peroxides.

Hydrides: In binary compounds with active metals hydrogen forms an ion with a charge of -1. Therefore H appears second in these formulas sodium hydride $\overset{1}{Na}\ \overset{1}{H} \longrightarrow NaH$

calcium hydride $\overset{2}{Ca}\ \overset{1}{H} \longrightarrow CaH_2$

Peroxides: A "normal" oxide contains the element with its usual valence as in sodium oxide $\overset{1}{Na}\!\!\times\!\!\overset{2}{O} \longrightarrow Na_2O$

The peroxide, sodium peroxide is written by adding 1 O atom to the normal oxide formula, Na_2O_2. Similarly if barium oxide is BaO, barium peroxide is BaO_2. Hydrogen peroxide is H_2O_2, then hydrogen oxide (water) is H_2O.

Binary Acids: Some covalent gases react with water to form acids.

Gas	Formula	Acid (same formula)
hydrogen fluoride	HF	hydrofluoric acid
hydrogen chloride	HCl	hydrochloric acid
hydrogen bromide	HBr	hydrobromic acid
hydrogen iodide	HI	hydriodic acid
hydrogen sulfide	H_2S	hydrosulfuric acid

The binary acid molecules in water provide H_3O^+ hydronium ions, and negative ions (anions) otherwise called the acid radicals. Examples: hydrochloric acid HCl with water H_2O gives H_3O^+ and Cl^-. The acid radical or anion is the Cl^- and has a valence of -1. Hydrobromic acid HBr in water gives H_3O^+ and Br^-. The acid radical is the bromide anion Br^- and has valence -1.

OXY-ACIDS

These acids contain hydrogen, a nonmetal and oxygen. In water they yield H_3O^+ ions and acid radicals or anions as shown in the table:

Acid Forming Molecule in Water		Hydronium Ions →	Acid + Radical	Valence of Radical
hydrogen nitrate (nitric acid)	HNO_3	H_3O^+	NO_3^- (nitrate)	-1
Hydrogen chlorate (chloric acid)	$HClO_3$	H_3O^+	ClO_3^- (chlorate)	-1
hydrogen acetate (acetic acid)	CH_3COOH	H_3O^+	CH_3COO^- (acetate)	-1
hydrogen sulfate (sulfuric acid)	H_2SO_4	$2H_3O^+$	SO_4^{2-} (sulfate)	-2
hydrogen carbonate (carbonic acid)	H_2CO_3	$2H_3O^+$	CO_3^{2-} (carbonate)	-2
hydrogen phosphate (phosphoric acid)	H_3PO_4	$3H_3O^+$	PO_4^{3-} (phosphate)	-3

These oxy-acids with name ending -ic give acid radicals with name ending -ate.

The valence of the acid radical is equal to the number of hydrogen atoms lost from the acid molecule as hydronium ions.

Oxy-Acids of Chlorine and other Halogens: The halogen family is fluorine F, chlorine Cl, bromine Br, iodine I, and astatine At. Formulas of the oxy-acids that exist for the other halogens follow the same naming pattern as for the oxy-acids of chlorine.

perchloric acid	chloric acid	chlorous acid	hypochlorous acid
$HClO_4$	$HClO_3$	$HClO_2$	$HClO$
perchlorate radical	chlorate radical	chlorite radical	hypochlorite radical
ClO_4^-	ClO_3^-	ClO_2^-	ClO^-

Each acid radical has a valence -1. Perchloric acid has 1 more O atom than chloric. Chlorous acid has 1 less O atom than $HClO_3$, and the hypochlorous acid has 2 less O atoms than the chloric acid. This rule applies for the other oxy-halogen acids such as perbromic acid, bromic acid etc., The formulas are similar.

Similarly, sulfuric acid is H_2SO_4, sulfurous acid is H_2SO_3

nitric acid is HNO_3, nitrous acid is HNO_2

phosphoric acid H_3PO_4, phosphorous acid H_3PO_3, and

hypophosphorous acid H_3PO_2

If the acid name ends in -ous, the radical name ends in -ite.

Sulfate and Bisulfate: Acids which yield two or more H_3O^+ from one molecule can form more than one acid radical.

$$H_2SO_4 + H_2O \longrightarrow H_3O^+ + HSO_4^- \text{ bisulfate or}$$
$$\text{hydrogen sulfate radical}$$

or

$$H_2SO_4 + 2H_2O \longrightarrow 2H_3O^+ + SO_4^{2-} \text{ sulfate radical}$$

Similarly, sulfurous acid H_2SO_3 yields HSO_3^- bisulfite or hydrogen sulfite radical and SO_3^{2-} sulfite radical.

Carbonic acid H_2CO_3 gives bicarbonate or hydrogen carbonate ion HCO_3^- and carbonate ion CO_3^{2-}

Phosphoric acid, phosphorous acid, and hypophosphorous acid may each yield up to 3 H_3O^+ per acid molecule therefore

$$H_3PO_4 + H_2O \longrightarrow H_3O^+ + H_2PO_4^- \text{ dihydrogen}$$
$$\text{phosphate radical}$$

$$H_3PO_4 + 2H_2O \longrightarrow 2H_3O^+ + HPO_4^{2-} \text{ monohydrogen}$$
$$\text{phosphate radical}$$

$$H_3PO_4 + 3H_2O \longrightarrow 3H_3O^+ + PO_4^{3-} \text{ phosphate radical}$$

It follows that each acid that yields only one H_3O^+ per molecule forms only one family of salts. Acids such as sulfuric give $2H_3O^+$ per acid molecule and two different acid radicals, therefore two families of salts and so on.

Salts: A salt is made of an acid radical combined with a metal ion or ammonium ion (NH_4^+). The formulas may be written using the cross over rule. The metal ions show their valences as given in the table on page 39. The acid radicals are considered as units with valences independent of the actual number and kind of atom in the radical. Examples:

sodium nitrate, $\overset{1+}{Na} \times \overset{-1}{NO_3} \longrightarrow NaNO_3$

magnesium sulfate, $\overset{2+}{Mg} \times \overset{2-}{SO_4} \longrightarrow MgSO_4$ a 2:2 or 3:3 ratio

is simplified to 1:1.

potassium hydrogen carbonate, $\overset{1+}{K} + HCO_3^- \longrightarrow KHCO_3$

copper (I) acetate, $\overset{1+}{Cu} + CH_3COO^- \longrightarrow CuCH_3COO$

aluminum sulfate, $\overset{3+}{Al} + \overset{2-}{SO_4} \longrightarrow Al_2(SO_4)_3$

Because the acid radical SO_4^{2-} is treated as a unit it is kept in parentheses.

Similarly, tin (IV) perchlorate $\overset{4+}{Sn} \quad ClO_4^- \longrightarrow Sn(ClO_4)_4$

ammonium carbonate $\overset{1+}{NH_4} \quad \overset{2-}{CO_3} \longrightarrow (NH_4)_2CO_3$

Hydroxyl Ion: A water molecule provides hydroxyl ions OH^- with valence -1. Formulas of bases contain metal ions united with hydroxyl ions, and the usual rules apply.

Examples: sodium hydroxide $\overset{1+}{Na}$ $\quad\overset{-1}{OH} \longrightarrow NaOH$

calcium hydroxide $\overset{2+}{Ca}$ $\quad\overset{-1}{OH} \longrightarrow Ca(OH)_2$

ferric hydroxide $\overset{3+}{Fe}$ $\quad\overset{-1}{OH} \longrightarrow Fe(OH)_3$

Alternative Names and Prefixes

Certain elements have too many valences to be designated by the -ous and -ic endings. In these cases Greek prefixes are used to indicate the subscripts

mono	1	tetra	4
sesqui	1.5	penta	5
di	2	hexa	6
tri	3	hepta	7

Examples: CrO chromium monoxide, chromium (II) oxide, chromous oxide

Cr_2O_3 chromium sesquioxide, chromium (III) oxide, chromic oxide

CrO_3 chromium trioxide, chromium (VI) oxide

Similarly, PCl_3 is phosphorus (III) chloride, phosphorus trichloride, phosphorous chloride

Note the distinction between phosphorus — the name of the element, and phosphorous — valence of +3 for phosphorus.

Oxides of Nitrogen: These are nitrous oxide (laughing gas) N_2O, nitric oxide NO, nitrogen trioxide N_2O_3, nitrogen dioxide NO_2 (or dinitrogen tetroxide N_2O_4). and nitrogen pentoxide N_2O_5.

EQUATIONS

A chemical equation is a short method of stating some features of a reaction. The formulas on the left show the reactants present before the change, and the products are shown on the right.

Example: sodium + water $\longrightarrow$ sodium hydroxide + hydrogen

reactants $\qquad\qquad\qquad\qquad$ products

A chemical equation must be balanced. That is, the total of all atoms on the left must appear on the right. This follows from a fundamental law of chemistry, the Law of Conservation of Matter: matter is neither created nor destroyed in any chemical change.

EXPERIMENT TO VERIFY THE LAW OF CONSERVATION OF MATTER

Set up a stoppered flask with two separate solutions.

Suitable pairs of solutions are:

(i) lead nitrate and potassium iodide.

(ii) sodium chloride and silver nitrate

(iii) copper sulfate and sodium hydroxide

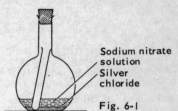

Sodium nitrate solution
Silver chloride

Fig. 6-1

The closed system (stoppered flask and contents) is weighed accurately. Then it is tilted to cause a reaction. In each case a solid product forms from the solutions. The flask and products is weighed accurately again. There should be no change in weight indicating that within the limits of accuracy of the balance, the law of conservation of matter appears to be true.

Balancing Equations

(i) Write down all correct formulas after the equation in words

$$\text{lead nitrate + potassium iodide} \longrightarrow \text{lead iodide + potassium nitrate}$$

$$Pb(NO_3)_2 + KI \longrightarrow PbI_2\downarrow + KNO_3$$

This is the skeleton equation.

The downward arrow after a formula as in $PbI_2\downarrow$ indicates that the substance is insoluble in water and is precipitated.

(ii) Check if all reactant atoms reappear on the right. In this equation there are 2 I atoms in PbI_2 but only one I atom on the left. Similarly 2 NO_3 radicals appear on the left, but one on the right. Balance atoms only by changing the numbers of molecules. That is by writing numbers in front of formulas, never by altering formulas.

Then $Pb(NO_3)_2 + 2KI \longrightarrow PbI_2\downarrow + KNO_3$ has the I atoms balanced. Finally, 2 in front of the KNO_3 balances the whole equation

$$Pb(NO_3)_2 + 2KI \longrightarrow PbI_2\downarrow + 2KNO_3$$

Example:

$$\text{iron (III) oxide + sulfuric acid} \longrightarrow \text{iron (III) sulfate + water}$$

skeleton equation: correct formulas

$$Fe_2O_3 + H_2SO_4 \longrightarrow Fe_2(SO_4)_3 + H_2O$$

The equation is unbalanced. 3 SO_4 groups on the right require 3 molecules of H_2SO_4. Therefore,

$$Fe_2O_3 + 3H_2SO_4 \longrightarrow Fe_2(SO_4)_3 + H_2O$$

Finally, $3H_2SO_4$ yield 6 H atoms and therefore 3 H_2O balanced equation:

$$Fe_2O_3 + 3H_2SO_4 \longrightarrow Fe_2(SO_4)_3 + 3H_2O$$

The correct ratio of formulas in a balanced equation may be verified experimentally, page 64.

7. OXYGEN, HYDROGEN

OXYGEN

Occurrence: Oxygen is the most abundant element on earth. It forms a major part of the earth's crust as well as being 8/9 of the weight of all water on earth and forming about 20% of the air by volume.

Atomic Structure: The atom has atomic number 8 and therefore has 8 protons in the nucleus and 8 electrons arranged K(2), L(6). The commonest isotope is O-16 with 8 neutrons in the nucleus. The O atom may gain 2 electrons from active metals to complete the L shell, or oxygen atoms may share two pairs of electrons as in oxygen gas O_2,

$\ddot{O}::\ddot{O}$ and carbon dioxide CO_2, $\ddot{O}::C::\ddot{O}$

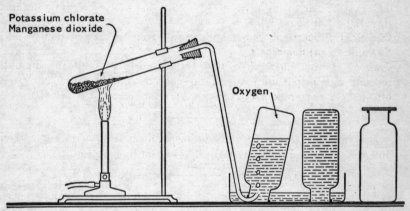

Potassium chlorate
Manganese dioxide

Oxygen

Fig. 7-1

Preparation of Oxygen

The gas is set free when some compounds are heated.

1. Mercury (II) oxide, a red powder is strongly heated in a test tube. The powder blackens and disappears. At the same time a glowing wood splint inserted in the test tube catches fire. This test identifies oxygen. Silvery beads of mercury form on the cooler parts of the test tube.

$$2HgO \longrightarrow 2Hg + O_2$$

2. A usual method of making oxygen is to heat a mixture of about 1 part manganese dioxide with 3 times its bulk of potassium chlorate. in the apparatus shown above.

The manganese dioxide acts as a positive catalyst by speeding the decomposition of the potassium chlorate, but the catalyst is finally regained unchanged.

$$2KClO_3 \longrightarrow 2KCl + 3O_2$$

potassium chlorate   potassium   oxygen
                         chloride

Identification Test Oxygen makes a glowing splint catch fire. This is not a distinctive test for oxygen because laughing gas, nitrous oxide N_2O, may yield its own oxygen readily and relight a glowing splint also. The specific test is to add oxygen to a solution of pyrogallol (pyrogallic acid) in sodium hydroxide. A deep brown color forms. This solution may be used to find the percentage of oxygen in the air. Shake the solution with a measured volume of air in a stoppered gas measuring tube. Open the tube inverted in water. Water rises to replace about 20% of the air in the tube.

Physical Properties: Oxygen is an invisible, odorless gas which is about 4% by volume soluble in water at room temperature. It is slightly denser than air in the ratio of 32 : 28.9 and has a boiling point and freezing point near -200°C.

Chemical Properties: Substances burn better in oxygen than in air.
Examples: (a) nonmetals
Carbon: If wood charcoal is strongly heated in air until glowing dull red and then is put into oxygen, the carbon burns brightly, and gives off sparks. The product is the invisible gas carbon dioxide.

$$C + O_2 \longrightarrow CO_2$$

This may be shown by shaking some lime water with the carbon dioxide. A white gelatinous (jelly like) solid forms.

$$CO_2 + Ca(OH)_2 \longrightarrow CaCO_3 + H_2O$$

lime water   calcium carbonate

Phosphorus: This substance is a fire hazard and is toxic. It should not be handled. Gently heat a small (rice grain size) piece of yellow (white) phosphorus in a deflagrating spoon and lower it into oxygen. There is a bright white flame and clouds of white smoke. Some of the red form of phosphorus may remain on the spoon.

The products are $P_4 + 3O_2 \longrightarrow P_4O_6$ phosphorus (III) oxide

$$P_4 + 5O_2 \longrightarrow P_4O_{10} \text{ phosphorus (V) oxide}$$

Sulfur: Some yellow sulfur crystals heated on a spoon will melt to a deep red liquid and burn with a pale blue flame and a choking odor. It burns brighter in a bottle of oxygen, and a cloudy gas sulfur dioxide forms.

$$S + O_2 \longrightarrow SO_2$$

(b) metals
Magnesium: Ignite a piece of magnesium in a Bunsen flame and

lower it into oxygen. An intense bluish-white light is seen and white smoke and powder of magnesium oxide forms.

$$2Mg + O_2 \longrightarrow 2MgO$$

Sodium: This metal is dangerous when wet and should never be handled. Cut a piece no bigger than a match head and heat it until it melts. When lowered into oxygen, a golden yellow flame is seen and white sodium oxide forms. Some yellow sodium peroxide may also form.

$$4Na + O_2 \longrightarrow 2Na_2O \text{ sodium oxide}$$

$$2Na + O_2 \longrightarrow Na_2O_2 \text{ sodium peroxide}$$

Iron: Strongly heated steel wool is quickly transfered to oxygen and burns with a golden glow and intense heat which may melt the metal.

$$2Fe + 3O_2 \longrightarrow Fe_2O_3 \text{ ferric oxide}$$

Acidic Oxides, Basic Oxides:

Non-metals such as carbon, sulfur, and phosphorus burn to form oxides classed as acidic. These oxides react with water to form acid solutions which turn blue litmus to red.

This may be shown by burning these elements in oxygen in a bottle and shaking the oxide products with water before adding litmus.

$$CO_2 + H_2O \longrightarrow H_2CO_3 \text{ carbonic acid}$$

$$SO_2 + H_2O \longrightarrow H_2SO_3 \text{ sulfurous acid}$$

$$P_4O_6 + 6H_2O \longrightarrow 4H_3PO_3 \text{ phosphorous acid}$$

$$\text{and } P_4O_{10} + 6H_2O \longrightarrow 4H_3PO_4 \text{ phosphoric acid}$$

Acid Anhydrides: The oxides CO_2, SO_2 etc., are called acid anhydrides because each may be regarded as the acid molecule without water.

$$H_2CO_3 - H_2O \longrightarrow CO_2$$

$$H_2SO_3 - H_2O \longrightarrow SO_2$$

Anhydride means without water.

Basic Oxides: Some metals form soluble oxides which react with water to form bases. The solutions turn red litmus to blue.

$$Na_2O + H_2O \longrightarrow 2NaOH \text{ sodium hydroxide}$$

$$MgO + H_2O \longrightarrow Mg(OH)_2 \text{ magnesium hydroxide}$$

Iron oxides are relatively insoluble in water and do not form bases.

Basic Anhydrides: Na_2O, MgO and other soluble metallic oxides are called basic anhydrides because they may be regarded as the result of removing water from the base. Example:

$$2NaOH - H_2O \longrightarrow Na_2O$$

base -- water $\longrightarrow$ basic anhydride

Industrial Source of Oxygen: Air is first compressed. This makes it warm up. Then it is cooled and suddenly allowed to expand. This causes further cooling. The cycle of compression, cooling, and reducing the pressure is repeated many times so that the temperature drops enough to give liquid air about $-200°C$. When liquid air is gradually heated the oxygen and nitrogen in it boil away at different temperatures. In this way large amounts of pure oxygen are obtained. The process is called the fractional distillation of liquid air.

Importance of Oxygen: The gas is important for life. All living cells use oxygen in respiration in which chemical changes in the cells release energy used to cause further chemical changes and release heat.

Oxygen is used in high temperature oxy-acetylene welding and cutting metals and in removing impurities in steel making. Other uses are as a rocket fuel and in oxygen tents in hospitals.

Oxidation: When an element or compound chemically unites with oxygen this is called oxidation. The rate of oxidation depends on the chemical activity of a substance, the temperature and whether the substance is finely powdered or not.

The noble metals gold and platinum are so inactive that they do not oxidize even after centuries. Sodium is so active that when freshly cut and exposed to air it rapidly dulls over the surface. The rusting of iron is a relatively fast form of oxidation.

Combustion: Any vigorous chemical change which gives out obvious light and heat is called combustion. Oxygen is not needed for all combustion reactions although most common combustions use oxygen. Examples: a mixture of hydrogen gas and chlorine gas exposed to bright light reacts explosively. Powdered antimony sprinkled into chlorine catches fire by reacting vigorously with the chlorine.

Spontaneous Combustion: Some substances while oxidizing at room temperature release enough heat energy to make the material catch fire. This is spontaneous combustion. In some cases the released heat is trapped in the oxidizing material and makes the temperature rise to the ignition point of the substance.

Examples: Oily waste rags may spontaneously ignite especially if there is poor circulation of air. Chemical decomposition of the oils and the cloth generates heat to cause burning. Damp hay may ignite because it chemically breaks down and at the same time traps the heat released.

EXPERIMENTS TO SHOW SPONTANEOUS COMBUSTION

1. A pea sized lump of yellow phosphorus is dissolved in a few ml of carbon disulfide and poured over a filter paper held by tongs. The liquid evaporates leaving the phosphorus in a finely powdered

form on the paper. Sufficient heat is released by the phosphorus oxidizing to make it suddenly ignite.

2. Sprinkle some cellulose cotton with sodium peroxide. Then pour a few ml of water over the powder. It reacts exothermically to release oxygen and spontaneously burns with the typical golden yellow flame of sodium compounds.

$$2Na_2O_2 + 2H_2O \longrightarrow 4NaOH + O_2$$

DUST EXPLOSIONS: These show that substances which in large lump form such as coal oxidize relatively slowly but if finely powdered may burn explosively because each flammable dust particle is surrounded by enough oxygen to cause rapid combustion.

Examples: in a flour mill a static electric discharge may ignite fine dust. Similarly coal dust in a mine may burn explosively if a spark ignites it.

Humidifying the atmosphere or good ventilation will prevent these explosions.

HYDROGEN

Occurrence: Hydrogen is by far the most abundant element in the universe. It is the main component of the sun and other stars. There is however, little free hydrogen in the earth's atmosphere but it does occur in many major compounds. Water is 1/9 hydrogen by weight. Petroleum is a mixture of many hydrogen carbon compounds, and all animal oils, fats, carbohydrates, proteins have hydrogen as an important part of their structures.

Atomic Structure: Hydrogen has the simplest atom with a nucleus of 1 proton surrounded by 1 electron. There is no neutron, and the mass of the atom is 1 amu. Separate H atoms do not stay apart at room temperature but form H_2 molecules by sharing an electron pair as in H:H, or H−H.

Heavy hydrogen or deuterium, sometimes represented by D or H^2 is a hydrogen isotope of mass 2 amu consisting of 1 proton, 1 neutron, and 1 electron. A third isotope is tritium which is very rare and radioactive. It has 2 neutrons and 1 proton in the nucleus, and like the other hydrogen isotopes has 1 electron. It may be shown as H^3.

Heavy water contains 2 deuterium atoms sharing electrons with an oxygen atom. Its formula is often shown as D_2O, and it occurs in ordinary water as about 1 molecule in every 5000. It is used to control the rate of uranium decay in nuclear reactors.

Preparation of Hydrogen:
1. Addition of Active Metals to Cold Water.
Sodium is a soft silvery metal which is kept under petroleum ether to prevent oxidation. It should never be handled because of its corrosive action on wet skin.

If a small piece of sodium no bigger than a match head is cut and dropped into water, it reacts violently. The beaker of water should be covered immediately with a glass plate to prevent dangerous molten globules of the metal from being thrown out. The metal melts to a small ball which moves about on the water surface giving a hissing sound as it releases hydrogen bubbles from the water. A few golden sparks may be seen as the sodium finally dissolves to form a slippery solution of lye (sodium hydroxide). The basic solution turns red litmus to blue.

$$2Na + 2H_2O \longrightarrow 2NaOH + H_2$$

Potassium: It resembles sodium but has a purple sheen when freshly cut and is also dangerous. When a very small piece of the metal is dropped on water it behaves like the sodium but releases more energy, enough to ignite the hydrogen gas. As the globule darts around the surface of the water it has a lilac tail of flame of burning hydrogen with some potassium vapor. A strongly basic solution of potash lye (potassium hydroxide) is formed.

$$2K + 2H_2O \longrightarrow 2KOH + H_2$$

Calcium: This metal reacts in a more controllable way in water. It is a brittle grey metal which turns white in air. In water it sinks, sets free hydrogen bubbles and gives a solution and cloudy suspension of the base calcium hydroxide.

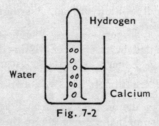

Fig. 7-2

Test tubes of hydrogen may be collected as shown, and tested with a burning splint. Also, if the liquid is filtered it may be shown to be lime water by blowing exhaled breath through the filtrate to cause the typical reaction of carbon dioxide gas with lime water.

$$Ca + 2H_2O \longrightarrow Ca(OH)_2 + H_2$$

Magnesium: Fresh powdered magnesium reacts slowly with cold water. A small spoonful may be added to a test tube full of water and this is closed with a one hole rubber stopper and left inverted overnight in a beaker of water. Enough hydrogen gas is released that it may be tested with a light.

$$Mg + 2H_2O \longrightarrow Mg(OH)_2 + H_2$$

Alternatively, an apparatus may be arranged to show that heated magnesium burns in an atmosphere of steam to form magnesium oxide and hydrogen. The apparatus is shown below.

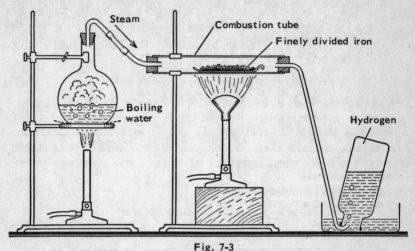

Fig. 7-3

At first steam is blown through the tubes to drive out air. Then the burners are lighted. Suddenly the magnesium catches fire and there is a rush of invisible gas over into the gas bottle. The gas burns with a slight pop indicating hydrogen. A strongly heat resistant combustion tube is required.

$$Mg + H_2O \longrightarrow MgO + H_2$$

Iron: Powdered iron or nails may be heated in the apparatus instead of magnesium. The reaction is less vigorous but again hydrogen is formed.

$$3Fe + 4H_2O \longrightarrow Fe_3O_4 + 4H_2$$
$$\text{magnetic iron oxide}$$
$$\text{ferroso-ferric oxide}$$

Reversible Chemical Changes:

The substances present before a chemical reaction are called the reactants, and the new substances formed as a result of the change are the products.

A chemical reaction is reversible if under one set of conditions the reactants form the products, and under different conditions the products react to produce the original substances.

The reaction of iron and steam is an example. Steam swept over heated iron gives magnetic iron oxide and hydrogen. The reverse reaction is to pass a current of hydrogen over the iron oxide. The oxide is reduced to iron metal by removal of oxygen, and steam is also formed.

2. Addition of Active Metals to Acids

Some of the more active metals such as magnesium, zinc, or iron set free hydrogen from dilute acids such as sulfuric or hydrochloric.

Put about a tablespoonful of granular zinc in the flask, and add enough dilute sulfuric acid through the thistle tube to cover the lower end. A vigorous bubbling occurs and the solution becomes hot. The bottles of hydrogen may be tested.

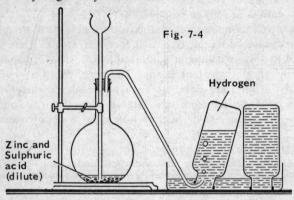

Fig. 7-4

Hydrogen

Zinc and Sulphuric acid (dilute)

$$Zn + H_2SO_4 \longrightarrow ZnSO_4 + H_2$$

Physical Properties: Hydrogen is an invisible odorless gas. It is insoluble in water and is the lightest of all gases. Its boiling point and freezing point are well below $-200^0 C$.

Chemical Properties: Hydrogen burns in air with a hot almost invisible blue flame to form water. This may be shown by allowing the flame to strike a cold surface. Droplets of water form. The water may be identified by adding anhydrous copper sulfate powder which turns blue.

$$2H_2 + O_2 \longrightarrow 2H_2O$$

Identification Test A gas is hydrogen if it burns to give water and no other product.

Hydrogen and chlorine gases in a mixture will react violently if ultraviolet light from bright sunlight or burning magnesium strikes the gases. The u.v. light provides the activation energy required to start the exothermic reaction.

$$H_2 + Cl_2 \longrightarrow 2HCl$$

This reaction, or the explosion of hydrogen with oxygen may be used to illustrate Gay-Lussac's law and prove the formulas for the water and hydrogen molecules (see page 67).

EXPERIMENT TO SHOW REDUCTION BY HYDROGEN

Use apparatus similar to that on page 52. Pass a stream of dry hydrogen over black copper (II) oxide in the tube. The hydrogen is dried by first passing it through U-tubes of calcium chloride or other drying agent. The powder turns red as copper forms. Droplets of water form on the cooler parts of the combustion tube.

$$CuO + H_2 \longrightarrow Cu + H_2O$$

One meaning of reduction is to remove oxygen from a compound. Other meanings are given on page 82.

Hydrogenation: Unsaturated carbon compounds have double or triple covalent bonds between some of the carbon atoms. These molecules may add hydrogen and form saturated hydrocarbon compounds which have only single covalent bonds. The term catalytic hydrogenation is used if a positive catalyst such as powdered nickel is used to help the change. **Example**: unsaturated vegetable oils are converted to solid saturated fats by adding hydrogen to double bonded carbon atoms.

Industrial Sources of Hydrogen: The gas is obtained by the electrolysis of water, but there are other more usual sources. Electrolysis of sodium chloride solution is also used. Both reactions are discussed in chapter 10, pages 82 and 83.

Another main source of hydrogen is by the thermal cracking of natural gas which is mainly methane CH_4. It is reacted with steam at a high temperature in the presence of a catalyst.

$$CH_4 + H_2O \longrightarrow CO + 3H_2$$

Then more steam is heated with the products at a different temperature and with another catalyst.

$$CO + 3H_2 + H_2O \longrightarrow CO_2 + 4H_2$$

The carbon dioxide may be dissolved in water under pressure to separate the hydrogen.

Uses of Hydrogen: Its use in the hydrogenation of edible oils has been given previously. Other unsaturated oils in crude petroleum are also hydrogenated to give useful compounds.

Hydrogen in liquid form is a useful rocket fuel because a relatively small weight of the gas burns to release large amounts of energy. In the oxy-hydrogen flame high temperatures are formed for welding or cutting metals.

A major use is the production of ammonia gas (Haber process). Nitrogen, obtained by the fractional distillation of liquid air, is mixed with hydrogen at $400°C$ and several hundred atmospheres pressure in the presence of a catalyst (iron powder and iron oxides).

$$N_2 + 3H_2 \longrightarrow 2NH_3$$

The ammonia may be oxidized to nitric acid which is another very useful chemical.

8. PERCENTAGE COMPOSITION, SIMPLE MOLECULAR FORMULAS, CALCULATIONS FROM EQUATIONS

ATOMIC WEIGHT, MOLECULAR WEIGHT, THE MOLE
ATOMIC WEIGHT:

This is the weight of an atom relative to the weight of the C-12 isotope taken as 12.0000 on the atomic mass unit (amu) scale. Atom weights are shown as O = 16, Na = 23 etc., and are listed on page 56. Some atomic weights are fractions as in Mg = 24.4 and Cl = 35.5. This is because most elements occur in nature as mixtures of isotopes (see page 14).

The Gram Atomic Weight (GAW) is stated in gram units of weight instead of the amu scale. **Examples**: Atomic Weight of Lead = 207 amu, GAW of Lead = 207 g. AW of Cl = 35.5 amu, GAW of Cl = 35.5 g. The importance of GAW is that 1 gram atomic weight of an element contains the Avogadro number (6.02×10^{23} atoms) of the element. **Example**: AW of aluminum = 27, GAW of Al = 27 g. Therefore 27 g of aluminum contain 6.02×10^{23} aluminum atoms.

The Avogadro number of particles is also called the mole. Therefore 1 mole of an element = 1 GAW of the element = 6.02×10^{23} atoms

Problems

1. What is the GAW of mercury, and how many mercury atoms are in 40 g of mercury? Hg = 200
   AW of Hg = 200 amu, GAW of Hg = 200 g
   1 mole of mercury is 200 g and contains 6.02×10^{23} Hg atoms

   40 g of Hg is $\dfrac{40 \text{ g}}{200 \text{ g}} = 0.2$ mole and therefore contains

   $0.2 \times 6.02 \times 10^{23}$ Hg atoms.

2. How many atoms are in 12 moles of sodium?
   The atomic weight is not required.
   1 mole of any element contains 6.02×10^{23} atoms
   12 moles of sodium contains $12 \times 6.02^{23} = 7.2 \times 10^{24}$ Na atoms

3. What is the weight in grams of 1.8×10^{24} atoms of sulfur? S = 32.
   6.02×10^{23} S atoms in 1 mole

   therefore, 1.8×10^{24} S atoms is $\dfrac{1.8 \times 10^{24}}{6.02 \times 10^{23}} = 3$ moles of S

   1 mole of S weighs 32 g, 3 moles weigh 96 g

ELEMENT	SYMBOL	ATOMIC WEIGHT	ELEMENT	SYMBOL	ATOMIC WEIGHT
Aluminium	Al	27	Lithium	Li	7
Antimony	Sb	122	Magnesium	Mg	24.4
Argon	Ar	40	Manganese	Mn	55
Arsenic	As	75	Mercury	Hg	201
Barium	Ba	137	Neon	Ne	20
Bismuth	Bi	209	Nickel	Ni	59
Boron	B	11	Nitrogen	N	14
Bromine	Br	80	Oxygen	O	16
Cadmium	Cd	112	Phosphorous	P	31
Calcium	Ca	40	Platinum	Pt	195
Carbon	C	12	Potassium	K	39
Chlorine	Cl	35.5	Silicon	Si	28
Copper	Cu	63.5	Silver	Ag	108
Fluorine	F	19	Sodium	Na	23
Gold	Au	197	Sulphur	S	32
Helium	He	4	Thorium	Th	232
Hydrogen	H	1	Tin	Sn	119
Iodine	I	127	Tungsten	W	184
Iron	Fe	56	Uranium	U	238
Krypton	Kr	84	Xenon	Xe	131
Lead	Pb	207	Zinc	Zn	65

NOTE: Memorize as many symbols as possible: refer to a table for atomic weights.

MOLECULAR WEIGHT, FORMULA WEIGHT

A molecule contains atoms united in a definite unit such as O_2, H_2O, C_3H_8 etc., The molecular weight of an element or compound is the weight of one molecule relative to the weight of the C-12 atom as 12.0000 amu.

Ionic compounds such as NaCl or network solids such as SiO_2 are given a formula weight calculated from the simplest ratio of atoms or ions in the compound. Formula weight is defined like molecular weight.

The molecular weight (formula weight) is calculated by summing the atomic weights of all the atoms in the formula.

Examples:

1. Calculate the molecular weight of glucose ($C_6H_{12}O_6$).
   C = 12, H = 1, O = 16
   molecular weight (MW) = (6 x 12) + (12 x 1) + (6 x 16) = 180 amu

2. What is the formula weight of potassium nitrate (KNO_3)?
   K = 39, N = 14, O = 16
   formula weight (FW) = (1 x 39) + (1 x 14) + (3 x 16) = 101 amu

3. What is the formula weight of bluestone (copper (II) sulfate pentahydrate)? $CuSO_4 . 5H_2O$
   Cu = 63.5, S = 32, O = 16, H = 1
   The .$5H_2O$ means 5 water molecules attached to 1 $CuSO_4$ unit
   FW = (1 x 63.5) + (1 x 32) + (4 x 16) + (5 x 2) + (5 x 16) = 249.5 amu

Mole of a Compound

1 mole of molecules will contain the Avogadro number of molecules. **Examples**: 1 mole of oxygen molecules O_2 contains $6.02 \times 10^{23} O_2$ molecules, 1 mole of propane C_3H_8 contains 6.02×10^{23} C_3H_8 molecules. As in the case of the relationship between AW and GAW, a similar rule applies to MW and GMW. **Examples**: the MW of carbon dioxide CO_2 is $12 + (2 \times 16) = 44$ amu, and its GMW = 44 g. The MW of glucose = 180 amu, and its GMW = 180 g. 1 mole of molecules = 1 GMW of the substance

Problems

1. How many molecules are in 4 g of oxygen gas? $O = 16$
   MW of O_2 = 32 amu, GMW = 32 g (1 mole)
   32 g(1 mole) of O_2 contains 6.02×10^{23} O_2 molecules

   $$4 \text{ g is } \frac{4g}{32g} = \frac{1}{8} \text{ mole and therefore contains } \frac{1}{8} \times 6.02 \times 10^{23}$$

   O_2 molecules

2. How many Na^+Cl^- units are in 0.25 moles of sodium chloride?
   $Na = 23$, $Cl = 35.5$ The formula weight is not required.
   1 mole of the compound contains 6.02×10^{23} Na^+Cl^- units
   0.25 mole contains $0.25 \times 6.02 \times 10^{23} = 1.51 \times 10^{23}$ Na^+Cl^-

WEIGHT IN GRAMS OF ATOMS AND MOLECULES

Atoms and molecules are samples of matter and therefore have mass which may be expressed in grams. 1 amu = 1.66×10^{-24} grams
Examples:

1. What is the weight in grams of a mercury atom? $Hg = 200$
   1 Hg atom weighs 200 amu = $200 \times 1.66 \times 10^{-24} = 3.32 \times 10^{-22}$ g

2. What is the weight in grams of the SO_2 molecule? $S = 32$, $O = 16$
   MW of SO_2 = 64 amu 1 SO_2 molecule weighs 64 amu
   = $6.4 \times 1.66 \times 10^{-24} = 1.06 \times 10^{-22}$ g

VOLUME OCCUPIED BY 1 MOLE OF A GAS

A sample of gas may be weighed and its volume noted at room conditions. From these results the gas density may be found and the volume occupied by 1 mole of the gas at STP.

EXPERIMENT TO MEASURE THE DENSITY OF A GAS

A light polythene bag of about 500 ml capacity is fitted with a one holed rubber stopper carrying a piece of tubing and a clip. The bag is squeezed empty and weighed accurately. Then oxygen from a cylinder is forced in to inflate the bag. It is left open but undisturbed to allow excess gas to escape and leave the bag full of oxygen at room temperature and pressure. The clip is closed and the bag full of gas is weighed accurately again. A graduated cylinder or bottle of more than 500 ml capacity is filled with water and inverted in water. The oxygen in the bag is expelled into the cylinder by compressing the bag. After adjusting water levels inside and outside, the volume of oxygen is noted. Room temperature and pressure are noted. The density of the gas in grams per liter at STP is calculated as shown on page 32.

1 mole of oxygen O_2 weighs 32 g. Knowing the density (weight of 1 liter of the gas at STP), the volume occupied by 32 g of oxygen is readily calculated. The result should be close to 22.4 liters at STP. The experiment may be repeated with carbon dioxide but in this case the volume occupied by 44 g(1 mole) of CO_2 is calculated. Again the volume occupied by 1 mole (1 GMW) of carbon dioxide at STP should be close to 22.4 liters.

GRAM MOLECULAR VOLUME

The volume occupied by 1 mole (1 GMW) of a gas at STP is 22.4 liters and is called the gram molecular volume (GMV). **Examples**: Hydrogen H_2 has GMW = 2 g and this weight of hydrogen has a volume of 22.4 liters at STP. Ammonia NH_3 has GMW = 17 g and this weight of the gas occupies 22.4 liters at STP. It follows that 22.4 liters at STP contains the Avogadro number (6.02×10^{23}) of molecules because 1 mole is the quantity of the gas.

If the formula of a gas is known its density, or the weight of any volume of the gas at any temperature and pressure may be calculated.

1. What is the density of carbon dioxide in grams per liter at STP?
   C = 12, O = 16
   CO_2 1 mole = 12 + (2 x 16) = 44 g and this occupies 22.4 l at STP

   $$\text{density of the gas} = \frac{\text{mass}}{\text{volume}} = \frac{44 \text{ g}}{22.4 \text{ l}} = 1.96 \text{ g/l at STP}$$

2. What is the volume occupied by 500 g of methane CH_4 at $25°C$, and 12 atm pressure? C = 12, H = 1
   CH_4 1 mole = 12 + (4 x 1) = 16 g, occupies 22.4 liters at STP
   apply the gas laws

   mass of gas = 16 g   mass of gas = 16 g

   V_1 = 22.4 l V_2 = ? l
   $\xrightarrow{\text{increases}}$
   P_1 =   1 atm P_2 = 12 atm
   $\xrightarrow{\text{increases}}$
   T_1 = $0°C(273°K)$ T_2 = $25°C(298°K)$

   $$V_2 = 22.4 \text{ l} \times \frac{1 \text{ atm}}{12 \text{ atm}} \times \frac{298°K}{273°K} = 3.23 \text{ l}$$

The mass of gas remains unchanged because the number of molecules is constant.

At 12 atm and $25°C$, 16 g of methane occupy   3.23 liters

then 500 g of gas occupies $500 \times \dfrac{3.23}{16} = 100.9$ liters

The alternative type of problem is that for a gas of unknown formula we may find its density experimentally by a procedure such as that on page 57. Then the GMW of the gas is the weight of 22.4 l at STP. **Example**: At $30°C$ and 764 mm Hg pressure, 420 ml of a gas weighs 0.35 g. Calculate the density of the gas in g/l at STP and its GMW.

$$\text{mass} = 0.35 \text{ g} \qquad\qquad\qquad \text{mass} = 0.35 \text{ g}$$

$$V_1 = 420 \text{ ml} \qquad\qquad\qquad\qquad V_2 = ? \text{ ml}$$

$$P_1 = 764 \text{ mm} \xrightarrow{\text{decreases}} P_2 = 760 \text{ mm}$$

$$T_1 = 30°C(303°K) \xrightarrow{\text{decreases}} T_2 = 0°C(273°K)$$

$$V_2 = 420 \text{ ml} \times \frac{764 \text{ mm}}{760 \text{ mm}} \times \frac{273°K}{303°K} = 381 \text{ ml}$$

381 ml of gas weighs 0.35 g   1 liter (1000 ml) weighs $1000 \times \dfrac{0.35}{381}$

$= 0.92$ g

density is 0.92 g/l at STP

The GMW is the weight of 22.4 l at STP $= 22.4 \times 0.92 = 20.6$ g

The number of molecules in any volume of a gas is readily calculated. 22.4 l of a gas at STP contain the Avogadro number of molecules.

Example: How many molecules are in 0.5 liters of hydrogen at STP?
22.4 l at STP contains 6.02×10^{23} molecules

$$0.5 \text{ l contains } \frac{0.5 \times 6.02 \times 10^{23}}{22.4} = 1.34 \times 10^{22} \text{ molecules}$$

If the volume is at another temperature and pressure it is first converted to STP.

COMPOSITION BY WEIGHT FROM FORMULAS

A pure compound has a constant composition. Therefore the ratio of the weights of the atoms in the formula is also the ratio of the weights in any sample of the compound. **Example**: Water H_2O contains 2 H atoms each weighing 1 amu united to 1 O atom weighing 16 amu in the formula of total weight 18 amu. Therefore hydrogen is $^2/_{18}$ and oxygen $^{16}/_{18}$ of the weight of 1 water molecule, and $^2/_{18}$ of the weight of any sample of pure water is hydrogen. Oxygen is $^{16}/_{18}$ of the water.

The weight composition may be expressed as percentages.

Example:

Find the percentage composition of potassium chlorate, $KClO_3$. ($K = 39$, $Cl = 35·5$, $O = 16$).

To find the percentage composition of potassium chlorate we must find (a) the formula weight, then using it, calculate (b) the percentage weight of each element present in the compound.

(a) Formula weight.

  K   Cl O_3

  39 + 35.5 + (3 x 16)
  39 + 35.5 + 48
  Formula weight = 122.5

(b) Percentage by weight of each element.

$$\% \text{ of potassium} = \frac{39}{122 \cdot 5} \times 100 = 31.8\%$$

$$\% \text{ of chlorine} = \frac{35 \cdot 5}{122 \cdot 5} \times 100 = 29.0\%$$

$$\% \text{ of oxygen} = \frac{48}{122 \cdot 5} \times 100 = 39.2\%$$

SIMPLEST (EMPIRICAL) FORMULAS

The simplest or empirical formula of a compound is the smallest whole number ratio of atoms in the formula. The actual molecular formula gives the number of atoms in the individual molecule, and is often called the true formula.

Substance	Simplest Formula	Molecular Formula
glucose	CH_2O	$C_6H_{12}O_6$
benzene	CH	C_6H_6
acetylene	CH	C_2H_2
water	H_2O	H_2O
hydrogen peroxide	HO	H_2O_2

Substances with different molecular formulas may have the same empirical formula (benzene and acetylene). The molecular formula and simplest formula may be identical (water).

Calculation of Simplest Formulas from Composition by Weight

The weight of each element in a sample of the compound is divided by the particular atomic weight. This gives the ratio of atoms of the different elements in the formula. If the ratio is not in simple whole numbers divide each term in the ratio by the smallest number. **Example**: find the simplest formula of a substance containing 29.1% sodium, 40.5% sulfur, and 30.4% oxygen. Na = 23, S = 32, O = 16

	Na	S	O
Weights	29.1	40.5	30.4

$$\text{Ratio of Atoms} \quad \frac{29.1}{23} \quad : \quad \frac{40.5}{32} \quad : \quad \frac{30.4}{16}$$

$$= 1.27 \quad : \quad 1.27 \quad : \quad 1.9$$

$$\text{Divide by smallest number} \quad \frac{1.27}{1.27} \quad : \quad \frac{1.27}{1.27} \quad : \quad \frac{1.9}{1.27}$$

$$= 1 \quad : \quad 1 \quad : \quad 1.5$$

$$= 2 \quad : \quad 2 \quad : \quad 3$$

Simplest formula is $Na_2S_2O_3$

MOLECULAR FORMULAS

The molecular formula of a compound is a simple multiple of the empirical formula. **Examples**: the molecular formula of benzene is C_6H_6 which is the simplest formula (CH) x 6, or $(CH)_6$. The molecular formula of acetic acid is $C_2H_4O_2$ and is the simplest formula (CH_2O) x 2, or $(CH_2O)_2$. If the simplest formula and the true molecular weight are known then the molecular formula is readily calculated.

Examples:

1. What is the molecular formula of ethylene glycol if the simplest formula is CH_3O, and the molecular weight is 62?
   molecular formula is (CH_3O) x n, where n = 1, 2, 3 ... or other integer
   MW of (CH_3O) x n = 62, or (12 + 3 + 16) x n = 62
   therefore, 31 x n = 62, or n = 2
   the true formula is $(CH_3O)_2$ or $C_2H_6O_2$

2. A compound of carbon, hydrogen, and oxygen was completely burned in oxygen. 0.45 g of the substance gave 0.86 g of carbon dioxide and 0.53 g of water. If the molecular weight is 46, calculate the simplest formula and the molecular formula.

   $\dfrac{C}{CO_2} = \dfrac{12}{44}$ therefore, weight of carbon in the compound is

   $\dfrac{12}{44}$ x 0.86 = 0.235 g

   $\dfrac{H_2}{H_2O} = \dfrac{2}{18}$ therefore, weight of hydrogen in the compound is

   $\dfrac{2}{18}$ x 0.53 = 0.06 g

weight of oxygen = weight of compound − (weights of carbon and hydrogen)

$$= 0.45 - (0.235 + 0.06)$$

$$= 0.155 \text{ g}$$

	Carbon	Hydrogen	Oxygen
weights	0.235 g	0.06 g	0.155 g
AW	12	1	16
ratio of atoms	$\dfrac{0.235}{12}$:	$\dfrac{0.06}{1}$:	$\dfrac{0.155}{16}$
	= 0.02 :	0.06 :	0.01
	= 2 :	6 :	1

the simplest formula is C_2H_6O
the true formula is (C_2H_6O) x n, such that the MW is 46
(24 + 6 + 16) x n = 46, therefore n = 1
the true formula is (C_2H_6O) x 1, or C_2H_6O

CALCULATIONS FROM EQUATIONS

A balanced equation shows the ratio of moles of the reactants and products. Therefore weights or volumes of reactants and products may be calculated. **Example**:

$$2Al(OH)_3 + 3H_2SO_4 \longrightarrow Al_2(SO_4)_3 + 3H_2O$$

$\quad$ 2 moles $\qquad$ 3 moles $\qquad\qquad$ 1 mole $\qquad$ 3 moles

Weight-Weight Problems

1. What weight of oxygen is obtained by the thermal decomposition of 2.45 g of potassium chlorate? K = 39, Cl = 35.5, O = 16

$\qquad\qquad$ 2.45 g $\qquad\qquad$? g

$$2KClO_3 \longrightarrow 2KCl + 3O_2$$

$\qquad\qquad$ 2 moles $\qquad\qquad$ 3 moles

$\qquad\qquad$ 1 mole $\qquad\qquad$ $^3/_2$ moles

$KClO_3$, 1 mole is 39 + 35.5 + (3 x 16) = 122.5 g

2.45 g is $\dfrac{2.45}{122.5} = \dfrac{1}{200}$ mole

therefore $\dfrac{3}{2} \times \dfrac{1}{200}$ moles of oxygen produced

1 mole of O_2 is 32 g, $\dfrac{3}{2}x\dfrac{1}{200}$ mole is $\dfrac{3}{2}x\dfrac{1}{200}$ x 32 = 0.24 g

2. How many grams of copper are required to produce 3 g of nitric oxide? Cu = 63.5, N = 14, O = 16

$$?g \qquad\qquad 3g$$
$$3Cu + 8HNO_3 \longrightarrow 3Cu(NO_3)_2 + 4H_2O + \qquad 2NO$$
3 moles $\qquad\qquad$ 2 moles

1 mole of NO requires $^3/_2$ moles of Cu. NO, 1 mole is 30 g

3g of NO is $\dfrac{3}{30} = \dfrac{1}{10}$ mole therefore $\dfrac{3 \times 1}{2 \quad 10}$ mole of Cu needed

weight of copper is $\dfrac{3}{2} \times \dfrac{1}{10} \times 63.5 = 9.53$ g

Weight-Volume Problems

1. What volume of carbon dioxide is formed at STP by the fermentation of 36 g of glucose? C = 12, H = 1, O = 16

$$36g \qquad\qquad ? \text{ liters at STP}$$
$$C_6H_{12}O_6 \longrightarrow 2C_2H_5OH + 2CO_2$$
1 mole $\qquad\qquad$ 2 moles

1 mole of glucose is 180 g. 36 g is $\dfrac{36}{180} = \dfrac{1}{5}$ mole

therefore $2 \times \dfrac{1}{5}$ mole of CO_2 produced

1 mole of any gas at STP is 22.4 liters

$\dfrac{2}{5}$ mole of CO_2 is $\dfrac{2}{5} \times 22.4 = 8.96$ liters at STP

2. What volume of chlorine is released at $35°C$ and 780 mm pressure by the reaction of excess concentrated hydrochloric acid on 8 g of potassium permanganate? K = 39, Mn = 55, O = 16, Cl = 35.5

$$8g \qquad\qquad ? \text{ l at } 35°C, 780 \text{ mm}$$
$$2KMnO_4 + 16HCl \longrightarrow 2KCl + 2MnCl_2 + 4H_2O + 5Cl_2$$
2 moles $\qquad\qquad$ 5 moles
1 mole $\qquad\qquad$ $^5/_2$ moles

1 mole of $KMnO_4$ is 158 g $\quad$ 8 g is $= \dfrac{8}{158} = \dfrac{1}{20}$ mole

therefore $\dfrac{5}{2} \times \dfrac{1}{20}$ moles of Cl_2 produced

$$\frac{5}{2} \times \frac{1}{20} \times 22.4 = 2.6 \text{ l at STP}$$

the gas volume is then converted to 35°C and 780 mm using the gas laws as on page 32.

Volume-Volume Problems

The volumes of gaseous reactants and products are in the same ratio as the numbers of moles in the balanced equation. This is independent of the actual temperature and pressure conditions as long as all volumes are measured at the same temperature and pressure.

1. What volume of oxygen is required at STP for the complete combustion of 20 liters of propane? What volume of carbon dioxide is produced? Molecular weights are not required.

	20 liters	? liters	? liters
	C_3H_8 +	$5O_2$ ⟶	$3CO_2$ + $4H_2O$
	1 mole	5 moles	3 moles
then	1 volume	5 volumes	3 volumes
	20 l	5 x 20 l	3 x 20 l

100 liters of oxygen used, 60 liters of carbon dioxide formed

2. What volumes of nitrogen and hydrogen are required to produce 600 liters of ammonia at 600°C and 200 atm pressure? The pressure and temperature conditions are not used.

	? l	? l	600 l
	N_2 +	$3H_2$ ⟶	$2NH_3$
	1 mole	3 moles	2 moles
	1 volume	3 volumes	2 volumes
	300 l	3 x 300 l	600 l (2 x 300 l)

300 l of N_2, and 900 l of H_2 required

EXPERIMENT TO VERIFY CHEMICAL EQUATIONS

1. Weigh a watch glass and then weigh it again with 1.5-1.7 g of barium chloride dihydrate ($BaCl_2.2H_2O$). Record the actual weight of the crystals, and dissolve them without loss in 25 ml of distilled water. Use the cleaned watch glass again to weigh about 1.5 g of silver nitrate crystals ($AgNO_3$) and record the actual weight. Dissolve this sample again without loss in another 25 ml of distilled water. Mix by pouring the barium chloride solution into the silver nitrate solution. A curdy white precipitate of silver chloride forms. It is light sensitive and goes violet after some minutes. Filter the precipitate through a filter paper to catch all of the solid. Wash it thoroughly with distilled water to remove any soluble salts and leave

the paper with silver chloride overnight to dry. Find the weight of the paper and residue. The weight of paper along may be found by weighing a similar dry one.

Sample Calculations:

weight of barium chloride dihydrate = 1.68 g

weight of silver nitrate = 1.52 g

weight of filter paper
+silver chloride = 1.64 g

weight of filter paper = 0.38 g

weight of silver chloride = 1.26 g

1 mole of silver nitrate, $AgNO_3$ = 170 g

1 mole of silver chloride, $AgCl$ = 143.5 g

$\dfrac{1.52}{170}$ (0.009) moles of $AgNO_3$ used, and $\dfrac{1.26}{143.5}$ (0.009) moles of AgCl produced.

The ratio of moles of $AgNO_3$: AgCl = 1:1

Excess barium chloride was used so that all of the silver ion in solution was precipitated.

To provide Cl^- for 1 mole of AgCl, 0.5 mole of $BaCl_2.2H_2O$ is needed.

Therefore, 0.5 mole $BaCl_2.2H_2O$ + 1 mole $AgNO_3 \longrightarrow$ 1 mole AgCl

or $BaCl_2.2H_2O$ + 2 $AgNO_3 \longrightarrow$ 2AgCl + $Ba(NO_3)_2$ + 2H_2O

1 mole　　2 moles　　　　　2 moles　1 mole　2 moles

9. WATER, WATER OF HYDRATION, SOLUTIONS, CONCENTRATION OF SOLUTIONS

WATER

OCCURENCE

This is one of the most important chemicals for life. Most of the chemical changes in living cells occur in water solution. Also water is very abundant as ice, water vapor, and liquid, and greatly influences our way of life and climate.

Molecular Structure A diagram of the polar water molecule is on page 21. Its structure may also be represented by an electron dot formula such as H:Ö:H or H:Ö:H

The unused electron pairs of the oxygen atom are called lone pairs, but are available to form definite hydrogen bonds to the relatively positively charged hydrogen atoms of neighboring molecules. Therefore water is called an associated liquid.

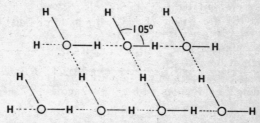

Fig. 9-1 Schematic Diagram of Hydrogen Bonding

ABNORMAL PROPERTIES OF WATER

Its molecular weight (18 amu) is quite small and we would expect water to be a low boiling gas like methane if the structure was non-polar covalent. However, hydrogen bonding and association of groups of water molecules make the boiling point ($100°C$) and freezing point ($0°C$) high. Another unusual feature is that ice is less dense than water. In the solid hydrogen bonds keep the molecules spaced apart. On melting ice some hydrogen bonds break and the molecules move closer together and the volume decreases until $4°C$ is reached. This is the temperature of maximum density of water. Above $4°C$ thermal agitation of the molecules makes them move apart. The breaking hydrogen bonds have a smaller influence on the volume and the water expands.

COMPOSITION OF WATER BY WATER BY WEIGHT AND VOLUME

Many experiments have been done to accurately measure the combining weight ratio of hydrogen and oxygen in water. The results show that hydrogen combines with oxygen in the ratio of 1:8 by weight. If this is expressed on the amu scale, then 1 amu of H reacts with 8 amu of oxygen. But the AW of oxygen is 16 amu, and the AW of hydrogen is 1 amu. Therefore in water 2 amu of H react with 16 amu of O, or 2 H atoms with 1 O atom to give H_2O.

The electrolysis of water (page 82) gives 2 volumes of hydrogen to 1 volume of oxygen. It follows from Avogadro's law:

water $\longrightarrow$ hydrogen   + oxygen

          2 vols   1 vol

          2n molecules   1n molecules

Equal volumes of gases at the same temperature and pressure contain the same number of molecules.

Therefore, water is composed of the two gases combined in the ratio 2n:1n, or 2:1 by molecules. This ratio is $2H_2:O_2$.

Then water is composed of hydrogen and oxygen in the ratio 4H:2O or 2H:1O. Other evidence indicates that the formula for water is H_2O.

GAY-LUSSAC'S LAW OF GAS VOLUMES

It has been shown experimentally for many gases that the volumes of gases in reactions are in simple ratios.

Gay-Lussac's Law: the volumes of gaseous reactants or products of a chemical change are in a simple whole number ratio if the volumes are measured at the same temperature and pressure.

Examples: water on electrolysis yields 2 volumes of H_2, to 1 volume of O_2. When hydrogen reacts with chlorine to form hydrogen chloride.

1 volume hydrogen + 1 volume chlorine $\longrightarrow$ 2 volumes hydrogen chloride

WATER OF HYDRATION

HYDRATES

Compounds which contain water as a definite part of the structure of the substance are called hydrates. **Examples**:

bluestone, copper (II) sulphate pentahydrate, $CuSO_4 \cdot 5H_2O$

Epsom salt, magnesium sulfate heptahydrate, $MgSO_4 \cdot 7H_2O$

hydrated sulfuric acid, $H_2SO_4 \cdot H_2O$

The $.5H_2O$ is interpreted as 5 molecules of water chemically attached to one unit of $CuSO_4$. The water is called water of hydration. If a hydrate is a crystalline solid, the water is called water of crystallization and this is not the same as irregularly trapped inclusions of water which form in some crystals as they are grown from solution.

Dehydration may be caused by gently heating a hydrate, and the residue is called the anhydrous compound (anhydrous, without water).

$$CuSO_4.5H_2O \longrightarrow CuSO_4 + 5H_2O$$

hydrated   anhydrous
salt   salt

If crystals containing trapped water inclusions are heated, the pressure of the heated water violently breaks up the crystals which begin to jump about. This is called decrepitation.

EFFLORESCENCE

If you examine crystals of photographer's hypo, sodium thiosulfate pentahydrate, $Na_2S_2O_3.5H_2O$ through a magnifying lens, and they have been freshly taken from the stock bottle, they appear glassy. After some minutes they appear chalky. Water is being lost to the room air.

This spontaneous loss of water of hydration is called efflorescence. The degree to which it occurs depends on the strength of chemical bonding in the hydrate, the temperature, and the relative humidity of the air.

The behavior may be explained thus; efflorescent hydrates have a vapor pressure greater than that of the room air, and they lose water until an equilibrium is reached.

DELIQUESCENCE

Substances such as calcium chloride or sodium hydroxide show the opposite kind of behavior. They adsorb water as a film on their surfaces and then dissolve in the water.

Example: pellets of soda lye (sodium hydroxide) examined through a magnifying lens appear wet in a few minutes. Make a highly humid atmosphere by standing a rolled paper towel in a beaker of water in a closed cupboard. If dishes of solid sodium hydroxide and calcium chloride are left there overnight they show strong deliquescence by forming solutions.

In these cases the first effect of the adsorbed water it form a low vapor pressure hydrate which therefore takes in more water to reach an equilibrium with the water vapor in the air.

HYGROSCOPY

Some substances attract water which clings to their surfaces. Either the substance is insoluble in the adsorbed water film or attracts so little that a solution does not form. This is hygroscopic behavior. Examples are silk, wool, glass, and silica gel which is particularly useful. Small capsules of silica gel are put in bottles of drugs to prevent spoilage by water. Also it is put in hifi speaker cabinets to prevent corrosion.

EXPERIMENT ON DEHYDRATION

The experimental procedure of part 1 on page 11 may be used to dehydrate a compound such as barium chloride dihydrate and verify that two water molecules are in the hydrate formula.

Experimental Results:

weight of evaporating dish   = 17.62 g

weight of dish +hydrated salt   = 23.05 g

weight of dish + anhydrous salt   = 22.78 g

weight of hydrated barium chloride   = 5.88 g

weight of anhydrous barium chloride = 5.16 g

weight of water of hydration   = 0.72 g

	Barium Chloride $BaCl_2$	Water
Weight	5.16 g	0.72 g
MW	208	18
Ratio of	$\dfrac{5.16}{208}$	$\dfrac{0.72}{18}$
Molecules		
	= 0.02 :	0.04
	= 1 :	2

the simplest formula is $BaCl_2.2H_2O$

SOLUTIONS

SOLUTION

A solution may be defined as a homogeneous mixture. For example if the blue powder copper (II) sulfate is added to water and left alone, a blue color gradually diffuses through the liquid as the solid disappears. In time the solution becomes a uniform blue shade throughout indicating that as a solution forms there is no tendency for the dissolved matter to settle under the pull of gravity. When the solution is examined through a powerful microscope, one phase only is seen because the dissolved particles are of molecular sizes. However the solution is not classed as a compound because we can vary the amount of added copper sulfate up to the limit of its solubility.

EXPERIMENTS TO SHOW CHANGES ON MAKING SOLUTIONS

Some types of physical changes are observed on making solutions. These do not all occur in making a given solution.

(i) Add a small crystal of potassium permanganate to water. A deep purple solution forms. The color is caused by the permanganate ion MnO_4^-.

(ii) If ammonium chloride powder or potassium nitrate is rapidly shaken with water, the temperature drops. When sodium hydroxide pellets are stirred in water, the solution becomes hot. There are two main factors for the temperature changes. Energy required to break bonds between the particles in the solid may come from the water and cause a cooling. On the other hand, the dissolving particles may become hydrated by bonding to water molecules and release energy as heat. It follows that the observed temperature change in making a solution will depend on the energies of hydration and dissociation.

(iii) A change in volume may occur on making a solution. If 50 ml of water is added to 50 ml of wood alcohol, the solution formed is slightly warmer but has a volume of about 98 ml. The attractive forces of hydrogen bonding between the two types of molecules draw them closer together although both liquids are usually classed as incompressible.

Other changes which occur on making solutions are these: Densities of solutions depend on the relative amounts of the solvent and solute. For example the state of charge of a car battery is often found by measuring the density of the sulfuric acid solution. Dissolved substances lower the freezing point of a liquid. An example is added ethylene glycol to water in a car radiator to prevent freezing. The boiling point of a solution is higher than the boiling temperature of the pure solvent.

Speeding Dissolving: This may be done by heating, stirring, or finely powdering the solute material. A large bluestone crystal will dissolve much faster in heated water than a similar crystal left standing in cold water. There are two factors. Increased temperature makes more water molecules collide with the crystal faces and detach solute particles. Also the vibrations of particles are greater in the crystal lattice as heat is added. Therefore they escape easily.

If a large crystal is finely powdered its surface area may be increased by a factor of 1000 or more. More water molecules can collide with the crystals and speed dissolving.

Stirring a solution prevents the region around the solid from becoming saturated and unable to dissolve more.

An undisturbed solution tends to become saturated around the dissolving solid and it becomes harder for molecules to dissolve. Stirring brings fresh unsaturated water around the solid and helps dissolving.

SOLUTION TERMS

The material that dissolves is called the solute and the substance in which it uniformly spreads is called the solvent.

Examples: sugar is a solute when it dissolves in the solvent water. Solid iodine is the solute when it dissolves in the solvent alcohol to form the brown solution called tincture of iodine.

A dilute solution has a relatively small amount of solute in much more solvent. **Example**: 6 grains of salt in a cupfull of water. A concentrated solution has relatively much more solute, as for example 4 tablespoonsfull of silver nitrate in a cupfull of water.

Unsaturated, Saturated, Supersaturated: An unsaturated solution is one which if placed in contact with a piece of the solute material will dissolve more. If a solution is saturated and an extra bit of solute material is added, it will remain unchanged. Supersaturation is a less common occurrence.

EXPERIMENT TO SHOW SUPERSATURATION

Not more than 10-15 measured drops of water are added to a test tube half full of hypo crystals (sodium thiosulfate $Na_2S_2O_3.5H_2O$). On shaking the mixture it cools and most of the crystals remain undissolved indicating that a saturated solution exists. Then the tube is heated gently until all of the crystals dissolve to form a hot unsaturated solution. If this is carefully cooled, without mechanical shock, to its original temperature we find that recrystallization does not occur. This cold solution is supersaturated because it has dissolved in it more crystals than were previously present in a cold saturated solution. However, addition of a single small seed crystal of the hypo upsets the unstable state of supersaturation and acts as a crystal nucleus for the excess dissolved solid to reappear. The seed crystal is seen to grow as it falls through the solution. A solution is supersaturated if addition of a piece of solute material causes crystal growth.

Solvents other than Water: The polar nature of water as a solvent has been discussed previously on page 24. Liquids such as benzene, kerosene, carbon tetrachloride and others are examples of nonpolar covalent compounds. In general they will dissolve other nonpolar liquids or solids but do not dissolve in water or dissolve water soluble substances such as sodium chloride. Mutually insoluble liquids such as water and gasoline are called immiscible. Water and ethyl alcohol are mutually soluble and are therefore miscible.

Emulsions: An emulsion is a mechanical mixture in which droplets of one immiscible liquid are suspended in another. Two liquid phases are seen if the mixture is observed under magnification. **Example**: vegetable oil shaken with water forms an emulsion. Hair creams and toothpastes are also examples.

Other Kinds of Solutions: A solution may be a homogeneous mixture of any phases although liquids are usual solvents. If two gases mix and do not react they form a solution. Air is a solution containing mainly nitrogen, oxygen and water vapor.

Gases form solutions in liquids. Natural water contains dissolved oxygen and carbon dioxide. Carbonated beverages are also examples. A solution of gas in a solid is less common. Hydrogen dissolved in the metal palladium is an example.

There are numerous examples of solutions of solids in liquids. Miscible liquids such as alcohol and water, or carbon tetrachloride and chloroform are liquid in liquid solutions.

Amalgams: The liquid mercury dissolves in metals such as silver and gold to form an amalgam. The same term is used for a solution of the metal in mercury.

Alloys: Some alloys are mechanical mixtures, others are classed as definite compounds, and there are alloys classed as solid solutions. Brass is a solid solution of copper and zinc.

CONCENTRATION OF SOLUTIONS

The concentration of a solution may be stated in different ways.

I. GRAMS OF SOLUTE PER 100 G OF WATER.

Example: A solution contains 45.0 g of potassium nitrate in 70.0 g of water. What is its concentration in g per 100 g water?

70.0 g water contain 45.0 g solute

$$100 \text{ g water contain } 100 \times \frac{45.0}{70.0} = 64.3 \text{ g}$$

The concentration is 64.3 g solute per 100 g water

Note that this expression of concentration is

$$100 \times \frac{\text{weight of solute}}{\text{weight of water}}$$

2. GRAMS OF SOLUTE PER 100 G OF SOLUTION.

Example: Use the figures of the previous example and state the concentration in g solute per 100 g of solution.

45.0 g solute, 70.0 g water, therefore 45.0 + 70.0 = 115.0 g of solution

since 115 g solution contain 45.0 g of solute

$$100 \text{ g solution contain } 100 \times \frac{45.0}{115} = 39.1 \text{ g solute}$$

The concentration is 39.1 g solute per 100 g solution

Note that this expression of concentration is

$$100 \times \frac{\text{weight of solute}}{\text{weight of solution}}$$

3. MOLAR CONCENTRATION.

This is more meaningful to the chemist because it gives the number of added solute molecules in a liter of solution.

A 1 molar solution contains 1 mole (1 GMW) of solute in 1 liter of solution, and therefore 6.02×10^{23} solute molecules.

Examples:

(i) What weight of sodium hydroxide is in 1 liter of 1 molar solution? Na = 23, O = 16, H = 1

1 mole of NaOH is 23 + 16 + 1 = 40 g

1 liter of 1 M NaOH contains 40 g solute

(ii) What weight of solute is in 5.0 liters of 0.1 M HCl?
 H = 1, Cl = 35.5
 1 mole of HCl = 1 + 35.5 = 36.5 g
 1 liter of 1 M HCl contains 36.5 g solute
 5.0 l of 0.1 M HCl contain 5.0 x 0.1 x 36.5 g =
 18.25 g pure HCl

(iii) How many moles of solute are in 200 ml of a 12 M solution?
 1 liter of 1 M solution contains 1 mole of solute
 200 ml (0.2l) of 12 M solution contains
 0.2 x 12 = 2.4 moles of solute

A general formula may be used to solve many molarity problems. By definition, the number of moles of a substance is

$$\frac{\text{weight of substance in g}}{\text{GMW of the substance}}$$ Example: 200 g of NaOH is

$$\frac{200 \text{ g}}{40 \text{ g}} = 5 \text{ moles of NaOH. The GMW of NaOH is 40 g.}$$

Therefore, since the molar concentration of a solution is the number of moles of solute per liter of solution the molarity

$$M = \frac{\text{weight of solute in g}}{\text{GMW x volume(liters)}}$$

Example: What is the molar concentration of a solution containing 2.8 g of potassium hydroxide in 250 ml of solution?
K = 39, O = 16, H = 1

GMW of KOH is 39 + 16 + 1 = 56 g   250 ml = 0.25l

$$\text{molar concentration, } M = \frac{2.8 \text{ g}}{56 \text{ g x } 0.25 \text{ l}} = 0.2$$

The formula contains 4 variables, molarity, weight of solute, GMW of solute, and volume of solution (in liters). It may be used to find any one of these quantities if the other three are known.
Examples:
(i) What volume of 0.4 M solution can be made by dissolving 120 g of pure hydrogen acetate in water?

Hydrogen acetate CH_3COOH C = 12, H = 1, O = 16

GMW of CH_3COOH (2 x 12) + (4 x 1) + (2 x 16) = 60 g

$$M = \frac{x \text{ g}}{\text{GMW x V(l)}} \qquad 0.4 = \frac{120 \text{ g}}{60 \text{ g x V(l)}}$$

$$V = \frac{120 \text{ g}}{60 \text{ g x } 0.4} = 5 \text{ liters}$$

(ii) What is the GMW of a solute if 2.5 liters of 4 M solution contain 160 g of solute?

$$4 = \frac{160 \text{ g}}{\text{GMW} \times 2.5} \qquad \text{GMW} = \frac{160 \text{ g}}{4 \times 2.5} = 16 \text{ g}$$

Solubility: The solubility of a substance is the weight required to make a saturated solution in a given weight of water at a certain temperature. The solubility of a substance is usually stated as the number of grams of solute required to give a saturated solution in 100 g of water at a given temperature. **Example:** at $20°$ C the solubility of potassium nitrate is 32 g per 100 g water.

Solubility of Gases in Water: Gases vary greatly in solubility. Some such as hydrogen and neon are regarded as being almost insoluble. Others such as ammonia and hydrogen chloride are very soluble. In all cases the solubility of a gas decreases as the temperature of the solution rises. Gases are more soluble in water if they are compressed. For example, a bottle of soda water contains compressed dissolved carbon dioxide. When the bottle is opened the sudden reduction in pressure over the solution makes the gas less soluble and it rapidly bubbles from the solution. For some gases the mass of gas dissolved in water varies directly with the pressure. Thus if the pressure of the gas is doubled the number of grams dissolved also doubles. This is known as Henry's Law.

10. ELECTROLYTES, ACIDS, BASES, SALTS

ELECTROLYTES AND NON-ELECTROLYTES

Electrical Conduction in Metals: In solid metals there are more readily available electron energy levels than the number of loosely held electrons. Therefore the outermost valence electrons are able to wander at random through the solid. When a source of electric potential energy is applied to the ends of a metal wire, the valence electrons still move at random but there occurs a gradual drift of electrons from the region of higher potential to the lower. The resulting directed flow of electrons through the wire is the electric current. The positively charged metal nuclei, and the inner tightly held electrons remain in approximately fixed locations in the solid. A metal is not chemically changed when a current flows through it, but may overheat and melt if too much current flows. *internal circuit*

Electrical Conduction in Gases: In gases such as neon at low pressure in a sealed tube, a high electric potential makes free electrons *current* (cathode rays) flow from the cathode (−) to the anode (+). At the same time positive gas ions are streaming towards the cathode from the anode. This is what is happening in a gas conducting electric current. There is no chemical change when the current flows.

Electrical Conduction in Liquids: A liquid or solution may conduct a current and if so, it is called an electrolyte. Other liquids do not conduct electricity and are called non-electrolytes.

EXPERIMENT TO IDENTIFY ELECTROLYTES

cation + ion)
anion(− ion)

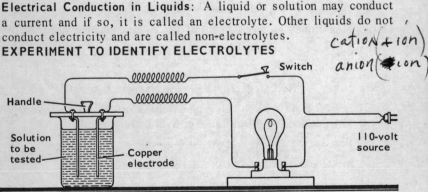

Fig. 10-1 Testing the conductivity of a solution.

The liquid is put into the beaker so that the metal wires are well below the surface. Then the current is switched on. If the liquid is an electrolyte, the bulb lights up. A current will not flow and the bulb does not glow if the liquid is not an electrolyte.

Suitable liquids for testing are solutions of sulfuric acid, hydrochloric acid, sodium hydroxide, potassium hydroxide, sodium chloride, sucrose (sugar), and the liquids methanol, ethanol, carbon tetrachloride. In addition distilled water and tap water may be tested. It is found that solutions of acids, bases, and salts conduct. The alcohols, and carbon tetrachloride are non-electrolytes, and so is distilled water. Tap water will conduct if the light bulb is low power (25 watt).

Electrolytes are solutions of acids, bases, and salts that conduct current by a directed flow of positive and negative ions in the solution. In addition, an electrolyte is decomposed by the current and chemical changes occur at the wires by which the current enters and leaves the solution.

Non-electrolytes are covalent liquids and do not contain ions to carry the current.

Distilled water is so slightly broken into ions that it is an extremely poor conductor. Tap water contains mineral salts in solution as ions that carry the current.

Ionic Solids: These substances do not conduct as solids because the ions are only vibrating and can not flow through the solid to act as a current. However, a molten solid has its ions free to migrate and will conduct and be chemically decomposed by the current. The electrolytic decomposition of compounds is taken on pages 82 - 84.

ACIDS, BASES, SALTS

ACIDS:

Some common properties of acids are

(i) sour taste like vinegar or lemons

(ii) blue litmus turns red, neutral (green) bromthymol turns yellow

(iii) carbonates and bicarbonates effervesce and release carbon dioxide

$$Na_2CO_3 + 2HCl \longrightarrow 2NaCl + H_2O + CO_2$$

(iv) active metals such as magnesium or zinc release hydrogen when added to sulfuric acid or hydrochloric acid

$$Mg + H_2SO_4 \longrightarrow MgSO_4 + H_2$$

(v) bases react with acids to form a salt and water

$$NaOH + HCl \longrightarrow NaCl + H_2O$$
$$\text{base} \quad \text{acid} \quad \text{salt} \quad \text{water}$$

(vi) water solutions of acids contain ions which make the solutions conductors of electricity

Hydrogen Ions: Acid forming molecules react with water molecules to give hydrogen ions. A hydrogen ion is simply a hydrogen nucleus or single proton. Because it is a very small particle of positive charge the hydrogen ion cannot exist alone in the electric field of water molecules but attaches to available electrons on the oxygen atom of the water.

$$H^+ \quad + \quad \overset{H}{\underset{H}{:\ddot{O}:}} \longrightarrow \left[\overset{H}{\underset{H}{H:\ddot{O}:}} \right]^+$$

The positive ion produced is H_3O^+ or $H^+.H_2O$ called the hydronium ion or a hydrated proton.

Therefore we may define an acid as a substance that yields hydronium ions in water. **Examples**:

$$HCl + H_2O \longrightarrow H_3O^+ + Cl^-$$
hydrochloric acid

$$HNO_3 + H_2O \longrightarrow H_3O^+ + NO_3^-$$
hydrogen
nitrate
nitric acid

$$CH_3COOH + H_2O \longrightarrow H_3O^+ + CH_3COO^-$$
hydrogen
acetate
acetic acid

Monoprotic acids give one hydronium ion per molecule. **Examples**: hydrochloric acid, nitric acid, and acetic acid. Although the CH_3COOH has 4 H atoms, only one breaks away as a hydronium ion, because it is attached to an O atom. The other 3 H atoms are united to a C.

Sulfuric acid and carbonic acid are diprotic acids that yield $2H_3O^+$ per molecule. **Example**:

$$H_2SO_4 + H_2O \longrightarrow H_3O^+ + HSO_4^- \text{ hydrogen}$$
sulfate ion

then $\quad HSO_4^- + H_2O \longrightarrow H_3O^+ + SO_4^{2-}$ sulfate ion

EXPERIMENT TO SHOW NEUTRALIZATION
This may be shown experimentally by this method:

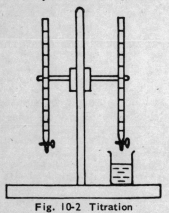

Fig. 10-2 Titration

A buret is filled to the zero mark with dilute hydrochloric acid. A pipet is used to measure 25 ml of a dilute solution of sodium hydroxide into a flask. Then 2 - 3 drops of litmus or other indicator are added to the base. While swirling the flask acid is slowly added from the buret until one additional drop of added acid just changes the indicator color from blue to red. This type of experiment is called a titration and the stage at which the litmus changes color is called the end point. There is just about enough base added to neutralize the acid to form a salt and water. If the solution in the flask is evaporated crystals of sodium chloride are obtained. They have the typical taste of common salt but may be slightly colored by the litmus.

$$NaOH + HCl \longrightarrow NaCl + H_2O$$

The original acid and base solutions are ionized and so is the salt water formed. Therefore a better representation is

$$Na^+ + OH^- + H^+ + Cl^- \longrightarrow Na^+ + Cl^- + H_2O$$
$$\text{or,} \quad Na^+ + OH^- + H_3O^+ + Cl^- \longrightarrow Na^+ + Cl^- + 2H_2O$$

If neutralization equations are written for other bases and acids it is seen that the reaction is simply hydronium ion combining with hydroxyl ion to form water molecules.

$$KOH + HNO_3 \longrightarrow KNO_3 + H_2O$$
$$\text{better} \quad K^+ + OH^- + H^+ + NO_3^- \longrightarrow K^+ + NO_3^- + H_2O$$
$$\text{or,} \quad K^+ + OH^- + H_3O^+ + NO_3^- \longrightarrow K^+ + NO_3^- + 2H_2O$$

The ions present unchanged before and after reaction are often called spectator ions because they do not play a direct part in the neutralization, although they are present with the hydroxyl ions and hydronium ions in the original solutions. In the last equation K^+ and NO_3^- are spectator ions.

A neutralization may be simply expressed as

$$H_3O^+ + OH^- \longrightarrow 2H_2O$$

Water molecules are very, very slightly broken into ions. Therefore bringing together large numbers of hydronium ions from an acid and many hydroxyl ions from a base gives a solution which cannot hold as many of both types of ions at the same time. Water molecules form.

BASES

Some common properties of bases are
  (i) bitter taste

 (ii) red litmus turns blue, neutral bromthymol changes from green to blue

(iii) some are slippery to touch

(iv) solutions of bases such as sodium hydroxide or potassium hydroxide will precipitate insoluble hydroxides of other metals from salts in solution

$$2NaOH + CuSO_4 \longrightarrow Cu(OH)_2\downarrow + Na_2SO_4$$

 (v) an ammonium salt heated with a base will liberate ammonia

$$2NH_4Cl + Ca(OH)_2 \longrightarrow CaCl_2 + 2H_2O + 2NH_3\uparrow$$

(vi) bases neutralize acids to form salts and water

$$2KOH + H_2SO_4 \longrightarrow K_2SO_4 + 2H_2O$$

(vii) solutions of bases conduct electricity because of the free ions present

Examples of bases are sodium hydroxide NaOH, potassium hydroxide KOH, calcium hydroxide $Ca(OH)_2$, and ammonium hydroxide NH_4OH.

Hydroxyl Ions: Bases in solution yield hydroxyl ions OH^-, and positive metal ions or the ammonium ion NH_4^+.

$$NaOH \longrightarrow Na^+ + OH^-$$
$$KOH \longrightarrow K^+ + OH^-$$
$$Ca(OH)_2 \longrightarrow Ca^{2+} + 2OH^-$$

The solid bases contain the ions which simply separate or dissociate in water. Therefore a better formula for a solid base would be $Na^+ OH^-$. Also the ions in solution become bonded to water molecules or hydrated and are often shown thus $Na^+_{(aq)}$ and $OH^-_{(aq)}$

Strength of a Base: As in the case of acids we distinguish between strength and concentration of a base. For example, a 1 M solution of sodium hydroxide contains 1 mole (40 g) of added NaOH in 1 liter of solution. This base is almost 100% dissociated to yield about 1 mole of hydroxyl ions

$$NaOH \longrightarrow Na^+ + OH^-$$

1 mole   1 mole   1 mole

A 1 molar solution of any substance has the Avogadro number (6.02×10^{23}) of added molecules in 1 liter of solution. Therefore 1M ammonium hydroxide has the same concentration as 1M NaOH solution. The ammonium hydroxide solution is less than 1% dissociated into its ions so that the hydroxyl ion concentration is less than 0.01 mole per liter.

The stronger base has a greater concentration of hydroxyl ions in unit volume of solution. If the apparatus of page 75 is used we may compare bases. The solution of a stronger base has more ions and gives a brighter light.

There is little evidence for the existence of NH_4OH molecules and a solution of ammonia is better represented.

$$NH_3 + H_2O \rightleftharpoons NH_4^+ + OH^-$$

SALTS:

Some salts are formed by neutralization and may be regarded as the compound of the positive ion from the base with the negative ion from the acid

$$Na^+ + OH^- + H_3O^+ + Cl^- \longrightarrow Na^+ + Cl^- + 2H_2O$$

$$\text{base} \qquad \text{acid} \qquad\qquad \text{salt} \quad \text{water}$$

The ions of the salt are shown separately because it is soluble and they are apart in the solution. In other cases if the salt is insoluble the ions leave solution together

$$Ba^{2+} + 2OH^- + 2H_3O^+ + SO_4^{2-} \longrightarrow Ba^{2+}SO_4^{2-} + 4H_2O$$

barium   precipi-
hydroxide   tated
solution

Common Properties of Salts: If salts have an ion in common they show similar behavior. Examples: $NaCl$, $NaNO_3$, Na_2SO_4 and so on give the golden yellow flame color of sodium if flame tested. But each salt will have different properties caused by the different negative ions Cl^-, NO_3^-, SO_4^{2-}.

Solutions of copper (II) salts are usually blue because of the color of the hydrated Cu^{2+} ion in water. Solutions of $CuSO_4$, $Cu(NO_3)_2$, and $Cu(CH_3COO)_2$ are examples.

Similarly, salts which form the same anion in solution as for example $NaCl$, KCl, $CaCl_2$ give Cl^- which reacts with a solution of silver nitrate to give white insoluble silver chloride

$$KCl + AgNO_3 \longrightarrow KNO_3 + AgCl\downarrow$$

$$\text{or } K^+ + Cl^- + Ag^+ + NO_3^- \longrightarrow K^+ + NO_3^- + Ag^+Cl^-\downarrow$$

Water and pH. Pure water is classed as a non-conductor because it has very, very few ions in it to carry electric current. At $25°C$, 1 liter of water contains only 10^{-7} moles of hydronium ion and also contains 10^{-7} moles of hydroxyl ion. This may be represented by the equation

$$2H_2O \rightleftharpoons H_3O^+ + OH^-$$

At any instant water molecules are breaking down to hydronium ions and hydroxyl ions, and at an equal rate ions are reuniting to form water molecules so that the actual concentration of H_3O^+ and OH^- is constant. But the concentration of unionized water molecules is about ten million times as great.

Water is taken as the standard neutral liquid because there is an equal concentration of hydronium ions and hydroxyl ions. [ ] means concentration

$$[H_3O^+] = [OH^-]$$

In acid solutions there are more hydronium ions than hydroxyl ions $[H_3O^+] > [OH^-]$ and bases contain $[OH^-] > [H_3O^+]$

In pure water at $25°C$, the product of the hydronium ion concentration and the hydroxyl ion concentration is

$$[H_3O^+] \times [OH^-] = 10^{-7} \text{ moles/1} \times 10^{-7} \text{ moles/1}$$
$$= 10^{-14} \text{ moles}^2/1^2$$

The value 10^{-14} is called the ion product constant. It is considered that approximately for all water solutions of acids, bases, and salts the $[H_3O^+] \times [OH^-] = 10^{-14}$. Examples: an acid may have $[H_3O^+] = 10^{-3}$ moles/1. Therefore its OH^- is

$$\frac{10^{-14}}{10^{-3}} = 10^{-11} \text{ moles/1}$$

Since 10^{-3} is greater than 10^{-11}, the solution is acidic. In a base solution the $[OH^-]$ might be 10^{-1} moles/1. It follows that the $[H_3O^+] = 10^{-14}/10^{-1} = 10^{-13}$ moles/1 and the solution has a much greater $[OH^-]$ than $[H_3O^+]$.

To reduce the work with negative integers, the pH scale is used. The pH of a solution is defined as the negative logarithm to the base 10 of the hydronium ion concentration expressed in moles/1.

Examples:

(i) If a solution of an acid has $[H_3O^+] = 10^{-4}$ moles/1 the

$$-(\log_{10} \text{ of the } [H_3O^+]) = -(-4) = 4$$

the solution has pH = 4

(ii) What is the pH of a solution if the $[OH^-]$ is 10^{-5} moles/1 and is the solution acidic or basic?

$$[H_3O^+] \times [OH^-] = 10^{-14}$$

$$\text{therefore, } [H_3O^+] = \frac{10^{-14}}{10^{-5}} = 10^{-9}$$

The pH is value of the index of the number 10^{-9} with the sign changed. That is the pH is 9.

Since the $[H_3O^+]$ is 10^{-9} which is smaller than the $[OH^-] = 10^{-3}$ the the solution is basic

ELECTROLYSIS

Electrolysis: This is the chemical decomposition of a compound in solution or a molten salt by passing an electric current through it. The Hoffman apparatus may be used to show the electrolysis of solutions of acids, bases, and salts. The electrodes are plates of platinum, or carbon, or lead which allow the current to enter or leave the solution. These substances do not react readily with the products of electrolysis.

Electrolysis of Water:

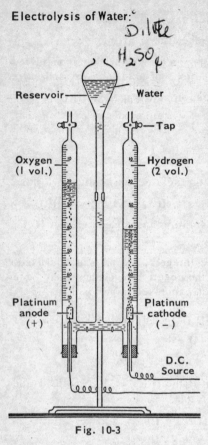

Dilute
H_2SO_4

Reservoir — Water

Tap

Oxygen (1 vol.)

Hydrogen (2 vol.)

Platinum anode (+)

Platinum cathode (−)

D.C. Source

Fig. 10-3

The negative plate has surplus electrons and is the cathode. It attracts positive ions (cations). The positive plate is the anode and it is short of electrons. It attracts the negative ions (anions). **Electrolysis of Water:** Pure water has very few ions and does not noticeably change if we attempt to pass a current through it. On addition of sulfuric acid to provide ions the current readily flows, and gases bubble up from the two electrodes.

Above the cathode an invisible gas collects, and it is found to be hydrogen by releasing some of the gas to an inverted tube and then applying a light. The gas burns with a slight explosion. Oxygen collects at the anode side. If allowed to run downward into a test tube the glowing splint test may be applied. The volume of hydrogen released is found to be twice that of the oxygen. This may be related to the equations which show that $2H_2$ molecules are released for every O_2 molecule. At a given temperature and pressure, 2n molecules of a gas will occupy twice the volume of n molecules of a gas (by Avogadro's law).

Ions in solution: H_3O^+, OH^-, SO_4^{2-}

AT CATHODE	AT ANODE
$4H_3O^+ + 4e^- \longrightarrow 4H_2O + 2H_2$	$4OH^- - 4e^- \longrightarrow 2H_2O + O_2$
The reaction at the cathode is reduction. Gain of electrons is reduction.	The reaction at the anode is oxidation. Loss of electrons is oxidation.

The sulfate ion is not discharged at the anode because it requires more electrical energy to make it react. As H_3O^+ ions are used up water molecules will break down to form more ions to replace those leaving the reaction system.

The net result is $2H_2O \longrightarrow 2H_2 + O_2$

The sulfuric acid is sometimes called a catalyst simply because it must be present for the reaction to proceed rapidly and it is not consumed. Note that we balance the reactions at the electrodes so that the gain and loss of electrons balances. Electrons are not destroyed in electrolytic reactions.

Electrolysis of Hydrochloric Acid: If this solution is electrolysed hydrogen gas forms over the cathode and a green solution and gas collects at the anode. The gas has the irritating odor of chlorine and bleaches litmus paper (a common test for chlorine). The green solution is chlorine water.

Ions in solution: H_3O^+, Cl^-, OH^-

At the Cathode: Hydrogen is formed as shown in the previous set of equations.

At the Anode: Less energy is required to oxidize Cl^- than OH^-

$$4Cl^- - 4e^- \longrightarrow 2Cl_2$$

There is 1 molecule of chlorine formed for every 1 molecule of hydrogen. The net result is

$$2HCl \longrightarrow H_2 + Cl_2$$

Electrolysis of Sodium Chloride Solution.

Ions in solution: Na^+, H_3O^+, Cl^-, OH^-

AT CATHODE	AT ANODE
H_3O^+ ions react as before	Cl^- react as before
Na^+ ions remain in solution	OH^- accumulate in solution

If some of the solution is removed from the cathode side we find on adding red litmus that the solution is basic. It is changing from a neutral solution of NaCl to the base NaOH as electrolysis proceeds.

The activity table (page 87) indicates that sodium metal is above hydrogen. Therefore a sodium atom will lose an electron more readily than a hydrogen atom. A result of this order also is that a hydronium ion gains an electron more readily than sodium ion. Therefore Na^+ remains in solution.

The net result is

$$2NaCl + 2H_2O \longrightarrow 2NaOH + H_2 + Cl_2$$

Electrolysis of Potassium Nitrate Solution: The products are hydrogen gas and oxygen gas. The K^+ ions and NO_3^- remain in solution and make it conduct. They are not discharged at the electrodes for the same reasons as given previously.

Electrolysis of Copper (II) Sulfate Solution: In this case we obtain a deposit of reddish metallic copper at the cathode and oxygen at the anode. The blue color around the cathode decreases.

$$\text{at the cathode } Cu^{2+} + 2e^- \longrightarrow Cu^0$$

The anode reaction was shown before.

In effect as this reaction proceeds, Cu^{2+} leave the system, and OH^- are also used up. H_3O^+ ions and SO_4^{2-} accumulate and the solution is changing from $CuSO_4$ to H_2SO_4. Therefore as electrolysis proceeds hydrogen and oxygen gases should be formed as in the electrolysis of water (page 82).

Electrolysis of Molten Salts: These reactions are important in industry for obtaining products too active to be liberated at the electrodes in a solution. Examples: electrolysis of molten sodium chloride produces sodium metal, and chlorine gas

AT CATHODE   **AT ANODE**

$$2Na + 2e^- \longrightarrow 2Na^0 \qquad\qquad 2Cl^- - 2e^- \longrightarrow Cl_2$$

The commercial production of magnesium (page 88) is another example.

11. IONS IN SOLUTION

REACTIONS OF IONS IN SOLUTION

Oxidation-Reduction Reactions: An oxidation is a reaction in which one or more electrons is lost by an atom or ion. Example:

oxidation of Na^0 (2,8,1) electrons to Na^+ (2,8) electrons

The zero over the Na indicates a neutral atom with no net charge. Reduction is the gain of electrons. Example:

S^0(2,8,6) electrons to S^{2-}(2,8,8) electrons

Electrons are not destroyed in chemical changes, therefore one reactant is reduced while some other reactant is oxidized. Some reactions previously given, may be expressed as reduction-oxidation or redox reactions. Examples:

$$Mg + 2H_2SO_4 \longrightarrow MgSO_4 + H_2$$

is better shown

$$\underset{\substack{2,8,2 \\ \text{electrons}}}{Mg^0} + 2H_3O^+ + SO_4^{2-} \longrightarrow \underset{\substack{2,8 \\ \text{electrons}}}{Mg^{2+}} + SO_4^{2-} + 2H_2O + H_2$$

Mg atoms are oxidized to Mg^{2+} ions by loss of 2 electrons to the hydronium ions of the acid. At the same time the H_3O^+ ions gain electrons and are reduced to water and hydrogen gas.
Addition of zinc to copper (II) sulfate solution

$$Zn^0 + CuSO_4 \longrightarrow ZnSO_4 + Cu^0$$

is better shown

$$Zn^0 + Cu^{2+} + SO_4^{2-} \longrightarrow Zn^{2+} + SO_4^{2-} + Cu^0\downarrow$$

The zinc atom is oxidized in giving 2 electrons to the Cu^{2+}, which is gaining electrons is reduced to copper.

These reactions are also classified as simple displacements because one atom replaces another in a compound.

Double Displacement Reactions: Two compounds in solution react to form two new compounds by an exchange of ion partners and one of the products is often precipitated. Examples are in the experiment on page 44.

$$\underset{\text{solution}}{Pb(NO_3)_2} + \underset{\text{solution}}{2KI} \longrightarrow \underset{\text{precipitate}}{PbI_2} + \underset{\text{solution}}{2KNO_3}$$

is better shown by the ionic equation

$$Pb^{2+} + 2NO_3^- + 2K^+ + 2I^- \longrightarrow PbI_2\downarrow + 2K^+ + 2NO_3^-$$

Again the reaction is not a redox because there is no change in valence or charge on any ion.

Reactions That Go To Completion:

Some chemical changes reach a state of equilibrium. Example: ethyl alcohol heated with acetic acid produces two products, an ester called ethyl acetate and water. As the reaction proceeds and the concentration of the product molecules increases, they tend to react and re-form the original substances acetic acid and ethanol. After a time a state of dynamic equilibrium exists at which the forward reaction and the back reaction are proceeding at the same rate. Although molecules are still reacting the concentration of each kind is constant.

$$\text{ethyl alcohol} + \text{acetic acid} \longrightarrow \text{ethyl acetate} + \text{water}$$

$$C_2H_5OH + CH_3COOH \underset{\longleftarrow}{\overset{\longrightarrow}{\rule{1cm}{0pt}}} CH_3COOC_2H_5 + H_2O$$

Other chemical changes do not reach an equilibrium of this type but proceed entirely from left to right. Several reasons may be given for this behavior.

1. Escape of a Gas

$$Zn + 2HCl \longrightarrow ZnCl_2 + H_2\uparrow$$

Hydrogen gas leaves the reaction system (the solution of acid), and the reverse reaction can not occur.

2. Formation of a Precipitate

$$AgNO_3 + NaCl \longrightarrow AgCl\downarrow + NaNO_3$$

The insoluble product AgCl in effect has left the reaction system (the solution) and prevents the reverse reaction from occurring to any noticeable extent.

3. Formation of a Less Active Element

$$Mg + FeSO_4 \longrightarrow MgSO_4 + Fe\downarrow$$

A magnesium atom is more active than an iron atom, in that the Mg will transfer 2 electrons to the Fe^{2+} ion of the $FeSO_4$ in solution. The Fe atoms produced can not transfer the electrons to the Mg^{2+} of the products, and the reaction does not reverse.

4. Formation of a Weakly Ionized Product

$$NaOH + HNO_3 \longrightarrow NaNO_3 + H_2O$$

In neutralization, the hydronium ions of the acid react with the hydroxyl ions of the base to form the very weakly ionized water molecules. Therefore the reaction does not readily reverse because of the slight tendency of H_2O to break down to ions. This is also considered on page 80.

The Activity Series:

The elements can be arranged in order of chemical activity which relates to the ease with which they gain or lose electrons.

EXPERIMENTS TO SHOW RELATIVE ACTIVITIES OF ELEMENTS.

1. Set up six test tubes containing dilute sulfuric acid. Add small amounts of the metals zinc, magnesium, lead, copper, iron, aluminum to each tube. Some of the metals react to displace hydrogen from the acid solution, and the relative rates of escape of hydrogen may be compared for the different metals. The order of activity is that shown on the activity table below.

2. The experiments of the section on hydrogen in chapter 7, on pages 50 - 54 show the relative activities of some metals with water or steam. Again the order of activity shown experimentally has been used to help make the activity table.

3. Metals such as magnesium, zinc, iron, copper etc., may be added separately to solutions of salts of other metals such as $FeSO_4$, $MgCl_2$, $CuSO_4$, $AgNO_3$, $ZnSO_4$ and observed to see if simple displacement reactions occur.

A metal is placed higher in the activity series if it will displace another metal from a salt in solution. Example: Copper is more active than silver.

$$Cu + 2AgNO_3 \longrightarrow Cu(NO_3)_2 + 2Ag$$

4. A more active halogen (chlorine) will replace a less active one such as bromine or iodine from solutions of bromides or iodides. Bubble chlorine gas into a solution of potassium bromide. The solution turns yellow because free bromine is formed.

$$Cl_2 + 2KBr \longrightarrow 2KCl + Br_2$$

The higher a metal is in the activity series the more readily it loses electrons(more readily oxidized). Therefore a metal higher in the series may give electrons to the ion of a less active metal.

1. K — Potassium		13. Co — Cobalt	
2. Na — Sodium		14. Ni — Nickel	
3. Ba — Barium		15. Sn — Tin	
4. Sr — Strontium		16. Pb — Lead	
5. Ca — Calcium		17. HYDROGEN	
6. Mg — Magnesium		18. Cu — Copper	
7. Al — Aluminum		19. Sb — Antimony	
8. Mn — Manganese		20. Hg — Mercury	
9. Zn — Zinc		21. Ag — Silver	
10. Cr — Chromium		22. Pt — Platinum	
11. Cd — Cadmium		23. Au — Gold	
12. Fe — Iron			

12. THE GROUP II METALS (CALCIUM AND MAGNESIUM)

This family is group IIA of the periodic table of the elements and contains the metals beryllium Be, magnesium Mg, calcium Ca, strontium Sr, barium Ba, and radium Ra in order of increasing atomic number.

Each metal has 2 electrons in the outer shell, and they are active metals which readily transfer the valence electrons to form ions with a charge of +2

MAGNESIUM

It is an abundant and useful metal. Sea water contains large amounts of magnesium chloride, and many regions on earth are composed of the mineral dolomite, $MgCO_3.CaCO_3$. It is obtained commercially by the electrolysis of molten magnesium chloride, $MgCl_2$, or by the Pidgeon process.

$$\text{at the cathode } Mg^{2+} + 2e^- \longrightarrow Mg^0$$

$$\text{at the anode } 2Cl^- - 2e^- \longrightarrow Cl_2$$

In the Pidgeon process, dolomite is roasted

$$MgCO_3.CaCO_3 \longrightarrow MgO + CaO + 2CO_2$$

An alloy called ferrosilicon which acts as a powerful reducer is heated with the mixture of solid MgO and CaO in a vacuum and the relatively low melting temperature magnesium sublimes

$$MgO + Si \longrightarrow Mg + SiO_2$$

Magnesium is a silvery-white metal of low density and it breaks easily.

Chemical Properties: The metal slowly oxidizes on exposure to air and becomes coated with grey oxide.

If a strip of magnesium is heated in air it begins to melt and then catches fire and burns with an intense bluish-white flame to form a white smoke and ash of magnesium oxide.

$$2Mg + O_2 \longrightarrow 2MgO$$

The electron rearrangements are

$$Mg^0 \quad + \quad O^0 \quad \longrightarrow \quad Mg^{2+} + O^{2-}$$

$$2, 8, 2 \text{ electrons} \quad 2, 6 \text{ electrons} \quad 2, 8 \quad 2, 8$$

The solid product is classed as an ionic solid and contains equal numbers of Mg^{2+} and O^{2-} held by electrical attraction.

The metal slowly reacts with water (see page 52).

Magnesium hydroxide solution (magnesia) is classed as a mild base.

$$MgO + H_2O \longrightarrow Mg(OH)_2$$

Magnesium reacts vigorously with acids, hydrogen is usually released.

hydrochloric acid

$$Mg^0 + 2H_3O^+ + 2Cl^- \longrightarrow Mg^{2+} + 2Cl^- + 2H_2O + H_2\uparrow$$

Magnesium Carbonate: If some of this white powder is touched to wet litmus there is no effect because it is insoluble. When strongly heated in the apparatus shown, bubbles of carbon dioxide are set free and turn the lime water a cloudy white at first. Then the cloudiness may disappear as soluble calcium hydrogen carbonate forms. The white powder residue in the test tube is magnesium oxide which turns red litmus to blue.

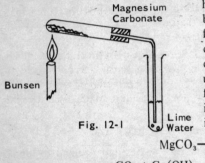

Fig. 12-1

$$MgCO_3 \longrightarrow MgO + CO_2$$

$$CO_2 + Ca(OH)_2 \longrightarrow CaCO_3 + H_2O$$
lime water   white
      jelly

$$CaCO_3 + H_2O + CO_2 \longrightarrow Ca(HCO_3)_2$$
      soluble

Magnesium carbonate shows typical behavior with acids. It effervesces and releases carbon dioxide.

$$MgCO_3 + 2HNO_3 \longrightarrow Mg(NO_3)_2 + H_2O + CO_2$$

CALCIUM

It occurs mainly as limestone, marble, and chalk which are all forms of calcium carbonate. Also it is found in the double carbonate dolomite.

It is a silvery-white metal of low density and is brittle. On exposure to air it becomes coated with white calcium oxide.

Chemical Properties:

It burns in air with a brick red flame and this coloration is used to identify calcium compounds.

It reacts vigorously with water. The reaction is discussed on page 51.

The metal is produced by the electrolysis of molten calcium chloride. The reactions at the electrodes are similar to the electrolysis of magnesium chloride (see page 88).

In forming calcium oxide from the metal the electron rearrangements are

$$Ca^0 \quad + \quad O^0 \longrightarrow \quad Ca^{2+} + O^{2-}$$

$$2,8,8,2 \quad 2,6 \qquad\qquad 2,8,8 \quad 2,8$$

Again as in the case of magnesium, the bond is classed as ionic because of the large difference in electronegativities of calcium and oxygen.

Calcium Carbonate: In its natural form as limestone it is used as a flux in the blast furnace production of iron. The calcium carbonate yields calcium oxide which combines with impurities such as silica from the iron ore to form the byproduct calcium silicate (slag).

If a small lump of limestone or marble is strongly heated in a small wire holder, the carbonate changes to calcium oxide and glows with a strong incandescence called limelight.

$$CaCO_3 \longrightarrow CaO + CO_2$$

Calcium oxide is called quicklime. On adding water or slaking quicklime, it swells, releases heat and becomes the solid calcium hydroxide or slaked lime

$$CaO + H_2O \longrightarrow Ca(OH)_2$$

A solution of slaked lime is called lime water and is used to identify carbon dioxide gas as described on page 47.

HARD WATER

Water is hard if it does not readily lather with soap. The cause is Ca^{2+} or Mg^{2+} ions in the water which react with compounds in typical soaps to form insoluble curds of 'calcium soaps'. Although the natural calcium or magnesium carbonates of some rocks are very insoluble in water, natural waters usually contain dissolved carbon dioxide which makes the water weakly acidic as carbonic acid. This has a slow dissolving action on the carbonate minerals to put Ca^{2+} and Mg^{2+} into solution in the water making it hard.

Temporary Hardness: This hardness is removed by boiling. It is found in water that contains hydrogen carbonate ion HCO_3^- as well as Ca^{2+} or Mg^{2+}. On heating the water

$$Ca^{2+} + 2HCO_3^- \longrightarrow CaCO_3\downarrow + H_2O + CO_2$$

The insoluble calcium carbonate is often precipitated inside hot water pipes or boilers and forms a cement-like scale which may eventually clog the pipes. A similar reaction occurs with Mg^{2+}. Since the heating in effect removes the ions causing hardness, the water is no longer hard and lathers readily with soap.

Permanent Hardness: If Cl^- or SO_4^{2-} ions are in hard water, boiling does not precipitate $CaCl_2$ or $CaSO_4$. Therefore permanent hardness can only be removed by chemical treatment of the water.

Removal of Hardness: Both types of hardness are removed by any of these methods

(i) Add sodium carbonate (washing soda). The reaction is between ions

$$Ca^{2+} + 2Cl^- + 2Na^+ + CO_3^{2-} \longrightarrow CaCO_3\downarrow + 2Na^+ + 2Cl^-$$

The product sodium chloride remains in solution as ions and since soaps are usually sodium compounds we do not get a reaction between soaps and Na^+ in solution.

(ii) 'Permutit' type water softeners contain grains of sodium aluminum silicate (zeolite). If hard water slowly passes through a tank of this material there is an exchange between the Ca^{2+} or Mg^{2+} of the hard water and the Na^+ of the zeolite. The water leaving the tank is soft. In time each grain has become coated with insoluble calcium aluminum silicate, and then the original zeolite is regained by running a strong solution of sodium chloride through the tank.

water softening stage

sodium aluminum silicate + calcium chloride

$$\longrightarrow \quad \text{calcium aluminum silicate}\downarrow + \text{sodium chloride}$$

regeneration stage

calcium aluminum silicate + sodium chloride

$$\longrightarrow \quad \text{sodium aluminum silicate} + \text{calcium chloride}$$

(iii) Water is de-ionized by passing it through ion exchange resins which are of two types. Cation resins remove all positive ions (except H_3O^+) and replace them by hydronium ions going into the water.

$$Ca^{2+} + 2Cl^- + \underset{\text{from resin}}{2H_3O^+} \longrightarrow 2H_3O^+ + 2Cl^- + \underset{\text{compound}}{Ca^{2+} \text{ resin}}$$

Grains of anion resin replace all negative ions by hydroxyl ions.

$$2H_3O^+ + 2Cl^- + \underset{\text{from resin}}{2OH^-} \longrightarrow \underset{\text{pure water}}{4H_2O} + \text{resin } Cl^- \text{ compound}$$

Soaps and Detergents: Soaps contain sodium salts of long chain fatty acids such as sodium stearate $C_{17}H_{35}COONa$ and sodium oleate $C_{17}H_{33}COONa$. The reaction with hard water is

$$2C_{17}H_{35}COONa + Ca^{2+} \longrightarrow \underset{\text{insoluble scum}}{Ca(C_{17}H_{35}COO)_2} + 2Na^+$$

The reaction wastes soap as well as depositing solids on clothing in the wash and staining fabrics.

Detergents are synthetic soaps which do not form insoluble compounds with Ca^{2+} or Mg^{2+}. Therefore a detergent gives a lather at once in hard water.

Plaster of Paris: Calcium occurs in nature as the mineral gypsum

$CaSO_2.2H_2O$. This is partly dehydrated by heat to form plaster of Paris

$$2CaSO_4.2H_2O \longrightarrow (CaSO_4)_2.H_2O + 3H_2O\uparrow$$

When a thick paste of plaster of Paris is made with water it reforms gypsum and in the process becomes a rigid mass of interlaced needles. In addition, there is a slight expansion making plaster of Paris useful for making casts.

Gradation in Behavior in the Alkaline Earths.

The metals of group IIA of the periodic table show increasing size in order of increasing atomic number, beryllium, magnesium, calcium and so on. There is an increasing activity because the larger metal atom has a lower ionization energy. It loses the two outermost electrons more readily. This may be shown by comparing the activities of magnesium and calcium with water (pages 51 and 52).

13. THE HALOGENS

HALOGEN FAMILY

The elements fluorine, chlorine, bromine, iodine, and astatine form the most chemically active family of nonmetals and are group 7 of the periodic table. They are called halogens because they occur in salts in the sea. Each member has 7 electrons in the outer shell and readily gains control of an electron from an active metal to help form a stable octet. Otherwise they complete the outer shell by forming a single covalent bond of a shared electron pair.

Fluorine: This is the most active of all the elements and has a strong electron affinity. It is very dangerous and poisonous and therefore is usually not prepared in an elementary chemistry course. However reactions and equations which apply to the other halogens are true also for fluorine, and as it is even more active we may readily predict its behavior without actually doing the reactions. Astatine is the largest member of the family, and is radioactive. For this reason and its rarity, few of its reactions have been studied.

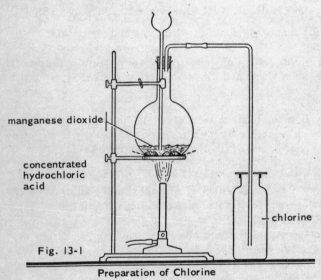

manganese dioxide

concentrated
hydrochloric
acid

chlorine

Fig. 13-1

Preparation of Chlorine

Chlorine: This occurs in sodium chloride in the sea and in salt deposits on land. Potassium chloride deposits also exist on earth.

Preparation of Chlorine

1. The gas is obtained by heating concentrated hydrochloric acid with manganese dioxide in the apparatus shown

$$MnO_2 + 4HCl \longrightarrow MnCl_2 + 2H_2O + Cl_2$$

The manganese dioxide acts as an oxidizing agent in the reaction and removes hydrogen from the acid.

2. A general method which is useful for making the other halogens may be used. Heat the sodium or potassium halide (sodium chloride) with concentrated sulfuric acid and manganese dioxide.

$$MnO_2 + 2NaCl + 2H_2SO_4 \longrightarrow MnSO_4 + Na_2SO_4 + 2H_2O + Cl_2$$

Physical Properties: Chlorine is a greenish yellow gas with an irritating odor, and is very poisonous. It is denser than air and dissolves in water to form a green solution called chlorine water. The gas may be liquefied by pressure alone at room temperature.

Chemical Properties: The gas is more active than bromine and iodine but less active than fluorine.

Bleaching Action: Wet colored flower petals or grass is bleached when put in a jar of chlorine. The active bleaching agent is hypochlorous acid formed in chlorine water

$$H_2O + Cl_2 \longrightarrow HCl + HClO \text{ (hypochlorous acid)}$$
$$\text{chlorine water}$$

The HClO oxidizes the dye molecule to a colorless structure.

$$\text{dye molecule} + HClO \longrightarrow \text{bleached dye} + HCl$$

Chlorine reacts vigorously with metals and nonmetals.

METALS

Copper: Heat a strip of copper and lower it into chlorine. There is a bluish-green flame and clouds of yellow smoke.

$$Cu + Cl_2 \longrightarrow CuCl_2$$

Sodium: If a small piece is heated on a deflagrating spoon and lowered into chlorine, the metal burns with the usual golden yellow flame of sodium and forms white clouds of sodium chloride.

$$2Na + Cl_2 \longrightarrow 2NaCl$$

Antimony: Powdered antimony sprinkled into chlorine catches fire. This is an example of spontaneous combustion not involving oxygen.

NON-METALS

Phosphorus: A small piece of yellow phosphorus ignites in chlorine to form the two chlorides. A bright flame is seen, and smoke.

Hydrogen: This gas reacts explosively with chlorine in the presence of bright light to form hydrogen chloride gas.

$$H_2 + Cl_2 \longrightarrow 2HCl$$

Chlorine reacts with hydrocarbons such as candle wax to remove the hydrogen, and form hydrogen chloride. At the same time clouds of carbon form. A burning candle lowered into chlorine burns with a red smokey flame.

Industrial Source: Chlorine is prepared by the electrolysis of brine. The reaction is given on page 83.

Uses: Chlorine is used for bleaching cotton, and wood pulp, and for making hydrochloric acid.

Bleaching Powder and Bleach: The formula $CaOCl_2$ is given to bleaching powder although it is a mixture made by reacting chlorine with slaked line.

$$Ca(OH)_2 + Cl_2 \longrightarrow CaOCl_2 + H_2O$$

Addition of a dilute acid to bleaching powder releases chlorine

$$CaOCl_2 + 2HCl \longrightarrow CaCl_2 + H_2O + Cl_2$$

Laundry bleach contains sodium hypochlorite. It is made by reacting sodium hydroxide with chlorine.

Identification Test: Chlorine is identified by its color, bleaching action on dyes and by its displacement reaction with bromides, and iodides (page 96)

Bromine: This halogen also occurs in salts in the sea. If chlorine is blown through sea water, it displaces the bromine. Air also blown through at the same time drives out the bromine vapor.

$$MgBr_2 + Cl_2 \longrightarrow MgCl_2 + Br_2$$

Bromine is a dark red liquid which readily vaporizes, and is very poisonous.

Chemical Properties: It may be prepared by the general method described on page 94, using sodium or potassium bromide instead of sodium chloride. The equation is similar.

Metals and nonmetals which react with chlorine, react less rapidly with bromine. The observations and equations are similar.

Identification Test: Bromine displaces iodine from solutions of iodides (see page 97)

The element is less electronegative than chlorine. It reacts with hydrogen only on heating.

Uses: Bromine is used in making photographic chemicals such as AgBr. It is used in making lead tetraethyl, the anti-knock constituent of gasoline.

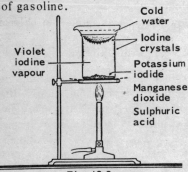

Cold water
Iodine crystals
Violet iodine vapour
Potassium iodide
Manganese dioxide
Sulphuric acid

Fig. 13-2
The laboratory preparation and collection of iodine.

Iodine: This halogen is also very active. It is mainly obtained from compounds in oil well brine or from sea weeds.

In the laboratory the general method of preparation is used, with sodium or potassium iodide as the salt. Because the element readily sublimes, it is collected as steely black crystals on the cold surface of the evaporating dish.

The element readily sublimes to a violet vapor at room temperature indicating weak van der Waal's forces between the molecules in the crystal. It is insoluble in water but dissolves in carbon tetrachloride, or chloroform to give a violet solution.

Identification Test: The color in CCl_4 solution may be used to identify iodine. Another test is its action on a suspension of starch paste. A blue colored complex compound forms.

Its chemical activity is less than that of bromine, it has a greater electronegativity, and a lower electron affinity. However it reacts readily with elements as in the case of chlorine or bromine.

Uses: It is used in drugs, dyes, and photographic chemicals. Also it must be present in small amounts in the human's diet to prevent the iodine deficiency disease of goitre.

Comparison of the Halogens: These elements may be compared in activity by several experiments.

EXPERIMENTS TO SHOW THE ACTIVITY OF THE HALOGENS

1. The relative reducing ability may be shown by heating the salts KCl, KBr, and KI with concentrated sulfuric acid.

Put a small amount of potassium chloride in a test tube. Cover the white crystals with concentrated sulfuric acid, and heat gently. There is effervescence, and choking steamy fumes of hydrogen chloride gas appear.

$$2KCl + H_2SO_4 \longrightarrow K_2SO_4 + 2HCl$$

This is not a redox because no ion or atom changes its valence or charge.

On repeating with crystals of potassium bromide, steamy choking fumes of hydrogen bromide, and the orange vapor of free bromine is seen. Some HBr produced by an equation similar to that above, acts to reduce the sulfuric acid.

The odor of burning sulfur (SO_2) may also be noted.

$$H_2SO_4 + 2HBr \longrightarrow 2H_2O + SO_2 + Br_2$$

In the example of potassium iodide, a more vigorous oxidation-reduction occurs. Hydrogen iodide reacts with the H_2SO_4 to give sulfur, hydrogen sulfide, and purple iodine vapor.

$$H_2SO_4 + 8HI \longrightarrow H_2S + 4H_2O + 4I_2$$

Again the HI may be regarded as formed by the same reaction as occurs with KCl and H_2SO_4.

2. Chlorine bubbled through potassium bromide solution sets free bromine. If carbon tetrachloride is added, the bromine mainly dissolves in this liquid to give an orange solution. This identifies bromine, as well as showing that the chlorine is more active.

$$2KBr + Cl_2 \longrightarrow 2KCl + Br_2$$
$$\text{or } 2K^+ + 2Br^- + Cl_2 \longrightarrow 2K^+ + 2Cl^- + Br_2$$

If chlorine is bubbled through potassium iodide solution, a dark brown deposit of iodine forms. It dissolves in CCl_4 to give a violet solution. This again shows that chlorine is more active. The equations are similar to the last two.

Bromine may be added to potassium iodide solution, and will displace iodine, showing that the smaller bromine atom is more active.

$$2KI + Br_2 \longrightarrow 2KBr + I_2$$

14. CARBON, CARBON DIOXIDE, CARBON MONOXIDE, ORGANIC CHEMISTRY

CARBON

Occurrence: There are more than a million known compounds of carbon. It is present in the atmosphere as carbon dioxide gas and is the essential element in living matter. Proteins, sugars, fats, mineral and vegetable oils are carbon compounds. It also occurs in rocks such as marble, limestone, and dolomite, and as diamond and graphite.

Atomic Structure: Carbon is element number 6 and therefore has 6 protons and 6 electrons in the atom. The C^{12} isotope is the commonest so that 6 neutrons are also in the nucleus. The element has the particular ability to form long chains and rings in which carbon is linked to more carbon by sharing of pairs of electrons, and for this reason there are so many carbon compounds that it is a separate branch of chemistry called organic chemistry.

CARBON DIOXIDE

This gas is about 0.04% of the atmosphere and also occurs in solution in natural waters as carbonic acid. It is an essential raw material for the process of photosynthesis by which plants make sugars and starches with the aid of chlorophyll and light.

Structure: The CO_2 molecule has the dot formula O::C::O and is a linear molecule. It is strongly covalent and nonpolar because of its symmetrical shape. Therefore as expected, it has a very low boiling point and freezing point and in the solid form as dry ice, there are weak van der Waal's forces between the molecules. For this reason, dry ice readily sublimes.

Preparation of Carbon Dioxide:

The gas is prepared by adding dilute hydrochloric acid to any form of calcium carbonate such as marble or limestone or chalk. The apparatus of page 53 is used.

$$CaCO_3 + 2HCl \longrightarrow CaCl_2 + H_2O + CO_2$$

Physical Properties: Carbon dioxide is an invisible odorless gas and is denser than air. It is fairly soluble in water.

Chemical Properties: The gas puts out flames if the temperature of the burning object is not very high. **Examples**: carbon dioxide poured from a bottle over a burning candle, puts out the flame. Burning magnesium is not extinguished in CO_2 because it is hot enough to decompose the gas and obtain the oxygen needed to maintain combustion.

$$2Mg + CO_2 \longrightarrow 2MgO + C$$

In water, the weak carbonic acid forms.

$$CO_2 + H_2O \longrightarrow H_2CO_3$$

Identification Test: Carbon dioxide reacts with lime water to form an insoluble milky white precipitate (see page 47).

Plants use the carbon dioxide of the air with water in the presence of chlorophyll to make the simple sugar glucose. Light provides the energy for the reaction. The sugar molecules unite to form the complex molecules of starches.

$$6CO_2 + 6H_2O \longrightarrow C_6H_{12}O_6 + 6O_2$$
$$nC_6H_{12}O_6 \longrightarrow (C_6H_{10}O_5)_n + nH_2O$$

The n represents a number of the order of 1000 molecules.

Carbonated beverages contain CO_2 dissolved under pressure. When the bottle is opened the gas escapes because it is less soluble at lower pressure.

Dry ice is solid CO_2 and is a useful refrigerant. In the fermentation of yeast during bread making, the gas is released and forms bubbles that make the dough rise. Similarly during the alcoholic fermentation of sugars, carbon dioxide is formed with ethyl alcohol.

$$C_6H_{12}O_6 \longrightarrow 2C_2H_5OH + 2CO_2$$
$$\text{glucose} \qquad\qquad \text{alcohol}$$

Fire extinguishers use CO_2 in the liquid form or as a foam. In the foam extinguisher aluminum sulfate and sodium hydrogen carbonate react to form a jelly of aluminum hydroxide and bubbles of carbon dioxide gas which are trapped in the foam. The jelly coats the burning material and puts out the fire.

$$Al_2(SO_4)_3 + 6NaHCO_3 \longrightarrow 2Al(OH)_3 + 6CO_2 + 3Na_2SO_4$$

CARBON MONOXIDE

This gas has the formula CO, and is formed by the incomplete combustion of carbon fuels such as wood, coal, gasoline in a limited supply of air.

Laboratory Preparation: Carbon monoxide is obtained by heating formic acid with concentrated sulfuric acid which removes the elements of water from the formic acid.

$$HCOOH \xrightarrow[\text{heat}]{\text{conc. } H_2SO_4} CO + H_2O$$

The gas may be prepared by the apparatus of page 53.

Physical Properties: It is an invisible odorless gas about the same density as the air, and is insoluble in water.

Chemical Properties: Carbon monoxide burns in air with a blue flame to form carbon dioxide.

$$2CO + O_2 \longrightarrow 2CO_2$$

It forms explosive mixtures if mixed with air or oxygen and ignited. The gas may be used as a r e d u c i n g agent for metallic oxides. **Example**: pass a stream of carbon monoxide over heated copper (II) oxide.in a combustion tube. The apparatus is shown on page 52. Escaping gas should be burned at the outlet tube because carbon monoxide is very poisonous.

Importance: Carbon monoxide is very poisonous particularly as it has no odor. It unites with the haemoglobin molecule of the red blood cells to form carboxyhaemoglobin, a stable compound. This prevents oxygen from reaching the body cells. Usually oxygen is carried through the blood as oxyhaemoglobin.

Water gas, a useful industrial fuel contains carbon monoxide and hydrogen. It is made by reacting coke (carbon) with steam.

$$C + H_2O \longrightarrow CO + H_2$$

Carbon monoxide is formed in the blast furnace reactions and helps reduce iron·oxides to iron.

ORGANIC CHEMISTRY

Hydrocarbons: These are compounds of carbon and hydrogen only. They are broadly classified as open chain (aliphatic) hydrocarbons and ring hydrocarbons (aromatics).

The open chain hydrocarbons are in three families: alkanes, alkenes, and alkynes.

Alkanes: These are saturated hydrocarbons with the general formula C_nH_{2n+2}. Saturated means that all C-C bonds are single covalent. Methane CH_4 is the simplest alkane.

$$\begin{array}{cc} H & H \\ \cdot\cdot & | \\ H\!:\!C\!:\!H & H\!-\!C\!-\!H \\ \cdot\cdot & | \\ H & H \end{array}$$

The molecule is not flat but has the H atoms located at the corners of a tetrahedron and the C atom at the center. Each C-H bond is polar but the molecule as a whole is not polar because of its symmetry. It has the typical properties of a nonpolar compound, low boiling point and freezing point, nonconductor of electricity and weak van der Waal's forces between the molecules.

Methane is the major constituent of natural gas, and burns to form carbon dioxide and water.

It reacts with halogens such as chlorine to form substituted compounds in which one or more hydrogen atom is replaced by chlorine atoms. **Examples**: CH_3Cl methyl chloride, CH_2Cl_2 methylene chloride, $CHCl_3$ chloroform, and CCl_4 carbon tetrachloride. Other members of the alkane family have similar physical and chemical properties.

Ethane C_2H_6 Propane C_3H_8

```
  H H              H H H
H:C:C:H          H:C:C:C:H
  H H              H H H
```

Butane C_4H_{10}

```
  H H H H
H-C-C-C-C-H
  H H H H
```

normal (n-butane)

```
        H
        |
    H - C - H
    H   |   H
    |   |   |
H - C - C - C - H
    |   |   |
    H   H   H
```

isomeric (isobutane)

Isomers are molecules with the same molecular formula such as C_4H_{10} but different structural formulas. The prefix n- is used for the isomer which does not have a branched C chain. As the chain length increases the number of isomers greatly increases.

Homologous Series: Members of the same chemical family which are represented by the same general formula, have similar chemical properties, and show a gradual change in physical properties such as density and boiling point form a homologous series.

Alkenes: This family is unsaturated because there is a C = C double covalent bond between a pair of C atoms in each member of the family. The general formula is C_nH_{2n}. and the simplest member is ethene (ethylene) C_2H_4. The next member is propene C_3H_6

```
              H H
              | |
H-C=C-H     H-C-C=C-H
  | |         | |
  H H         H H
```

Because a carbon atom has 4 valence electrons there must always be 4 bonds shown from each carbon in a correct structural formula.

The alkenes burn to form carbon dioxide and water. They also react to form addition compound by the double bond breaking open to make electrons available for single bond formation. **Examples**:

```
                        H H
                        | |
H-C=C-H+Cl_2 ------> Cl-C-C-Cl  ethylene dichloride
  | |                   | |
  H H                   H H
```

$$H-\overset{\overset{\displaystyle H}{|}}{C}=\overset{\overset{\displaystyle H}{|}}{C}-H + H_2O + (O) \longrightarrow H-\overset{\overset{\displaystyle H}{|}}{\underset{\underset{\displaystyle H}{|}}{\underset{\displaystyle O}{|}}}C-\overset{\overset{\displaystyle H}{|}}{\underset{\underset{\displaystyle H}{|}}{\underset{\displaystyle O}{|}}}C-H \quad \text{ethylene glycol}$$

(antifreeze)

Dilute potassium permanganate provides the oxygen atom (O).

Alkenes dissolve in concentrated sulfuric acid. This may be used as in the petroleum industry to separate the alkenes from the saturated alkanes. On heating, the compound regenerates the alkene.

$$C_2H_4 + H_2SO_4 \longrightarrow C_2H_5HSO_4 \text{ ethyl hydrogen sulfate}$$

$$C_2H_5HSO_4 \longrightarrow C_2H_4 + H_2SO_4$$

Alternatively, if the compound is heated with water, ethyl alcohol is formed.

$$C_2H_5HSO_4 + H_2O \longrightarrow C_2H_5OH + H_2SO_4$$

Polymerization: This occurs when many small molecules join to make very large molecules. When ethylene is heated with oxygen at high pressures, the ethylene units unite to form a molecule which is essentially an alkane with a MW of about 20,000. The polymer is called polyethylene.

$$nC_2H_4 \longrightarrow \ldots CH_2-CH_2-CH_2-CH_2 \ldots \text{ or } (\ldots CH_2-CH_2 \ldots)_n$$

polyethylene

Alkynes: The general formula is C_nH_{2n-2} and there is a triple covalent bond between two carbon atoms in the molecule. The alkynes are even more reactive than the alkenes because of the greater unsaturation of the triply bonded carbons.

Acetylene (ethyne) is the simplest member, C_2H_2 or $H-C\equiv C-H$. It is readily obtained by adding water to calcium carbide.

$$CaC_2 + 2H_2O \longrightarrow Ca(OH)_2 + C_2H_2$$

Calcium carbide is made from the common materials coal, and limestone by roasting coke with calcium oxide in an electric furnace.

Acetylene burns with a smoky flame, but in the oxy-acetylene torch gives a very high temperature for cutting metals.

Halogen atoms readily add to acetylene to form molecules such as $C_2H_2Cl_2$ and $C_2H_2Cl_4$. Also it may be polymerized to the ring compound benzene by heating in a copper tube.

$$3C_2H_2 \longrightarrow C_6H_6$$

Another important reaction is the addition of water to acetylene in the presence of catalysts to form the useful chemical acetaldehyde which is easily converted to acetic acid.

$$H-C\equiv C-H + H_2O \longrightarrow \underset{\underset{H\ \ H}{|\ \ |}}{H-C-C=O} \longrightarrow \underset{\underset{H}{|}}{\overset{\overset{H}{|}}{H-C-C}}\overset{\displaystyle O}{\underset{\displaystyle O-H}{\diagup}}$$

acetaldehyde   acetic acid

Alcohols: The functional group of an alcohol is a OH attached to a hydrocarbon chain. The most important alcohols are the simplest methyl alcohol (methanol) CH_3OH and ethyl alcohol (ethanol) C_2H_5OH. Therefore the general formula for a monohydric alcohol (one OH group) is $C_nH_{2n+1}OH$.

Methanol is made from carbon monoxide and hydrogen heated with a catalyst.

$$CO + 2H_2 \longrightarrow CH_3OH$$

Ethyl alcohol may be obtained from ethylene (page 102) but is mainly formed by the fermentation of sugar using yeast.

$$C_6H_{12}O_6 \longrightarrow 2C_2H_5OH + 2CO_2$$

Alcohols may be oxidized to aldehydes and then to acids. Example:

$$C_2H_5OH \longrightarrow 2CH_3CHO \longrightarrow 2CH_3COOH$$

acetaldehyde   acetic acid

Structural isomerism is possible beginning with C_3H_7OH with the formulas

$$\underset{\underset{H\ \ H\ \ H}{|\ \ |\ \ |}}{H-C-C-C-O-H}$$

$$\underset{\underset{H\ \ H\ \ H}{|\ \ |\ \ |}}{H-C-\overset{\overset{H}{|}}{\underset{}{C}}-C-H}$$

n-propyl alcohol   isopropyl alcohol (rubbing alcohol)

The two simplest alcohols are miscible with water because of the OH group common to water and the alcohols.

They are useful as solvents and as raw materials for making many organic compounds.

Ethylene glycol is an example of a dihydroxy alcohol with 2 OH groups (structural formula on page 102)

Glycerol (glycerine) has 3 OH groups $CH_2(OH)CH(OH)CH_2(OH)$, one on each carbon atom.

Carboxylic Acids: These are also called the fatty acids because some of the long chain members are in vegetable oils and animal fats. The general formula is $C_2H_{2n+1}.COOH$ and the COOH group is the carboxyl group. Formic acid, HCOOH or $H-C\overset{\displaystyle O}{\underset{\displaystyle O-H}{\diagup}}$ is the simplest Acetic acid (vinegar) is the second member of the family

$$\begin{array}{c} H \\ | \\ H-C-C{\nearrow}^{O} \\ | \quad\searrow{O-H} \\ H \end{array}$$

The simpler members are miscible with water probably due to hydrogen bonding with the H_2O molecules.

Acetic acid is prepared by air oxidation of acetaldehyde as shown in the equations on page 103.

Stearic acid $C_{17}H_{35}COOH$ is obtained from animal fats and is in soaps as its salt sodium stearate $C_{17}H_{35}COONa$.

Ethers: These molecules contain alkyl groups such as CH_3 or C_2H_5 united across an oxygen atom, as in $H_3C-O-CH_3$ dimethyl ether, and $H_5C_2-O-C_2H_5$ diethyl ether (common ether).

Esters: These compounds form by an acid reacting with an alcohol with the loss of a water molecule. Some are important as the natural flavours in fruits.

$$CH_3COOH \; + \quad C_2H_5OH \longrightarrow CH_3COOC_2H_5 + H_2O$$
$$\text{acetic acid} \quad \text{ethyl alcohol} \qquad\qquad \text{ethyl acetate}$$

Amino Acids: These are an important class of biological compounds because many of the structural tissues and body fluids of animals are made of proteins which are derived from amino acids. The simplest is glycine, and it contains the basic amino group $-NH_2$ as well as the acidic -COOH carboxyl group, H_2NCH_2COOH.

Carbohydrates: These compounds are grouped as sugars, starches, or cellulose. The simplest sugars are substances such as glucose or fructose with formulas $C_6H_{12}O_6$. Isomers are possible. Example: glucose has an aldehyde group $-CHO$ in its formula shown by the fact that it reduces cupric salts to cuprous. Therefore it is classed as a reducing sugar. Fructose has a different structural formula containing a ketone group $C=O$ and is not a reducing sugar. These simple sugars are also called monosaccharides. Note that the carbohydrates have 2H atoms for every 1 O atom, the same ratio as in water. The general formula for all carbohydrates is $C_x(H_2O)_y$.

Sucrose $C_{12}H_{22}O_{11}$ is a disaccharide which may be regarded as made of two simple sugar molecules united with the loss of water.

$$C_6H_{12}O_6 + C_6H_{12}O_6 \longrightarrow C_{11}H_{22}O_{11} + H_2O$$
$$\text{glucose} \quad \text{fructose} \qquad\qquad \text{sucrose}$$

These molecules also behave as if they had ring forms.

Starches contain many simple sugar linkages with the elimination of water. The general formula is of the type $(C_6H_{10}O_5)n$ where n is of the order of 1000. Cellulose has a similar type general formula with more units differently arranged. These are examples of polysaccharides.

15. PERIODIC TABLE

PERIODIC TABLE

Mendeleev's Periodic Table: About the year 1870, the Russian chemist Mendeleev arranged the known elements in a table such that elements in the same family occurred together and showed similar properties. He left gaps for elements yet to be discovered, and predicted properties for some of them. Later, when the elements were isolated, his predictions were found to be true. His table had the elements arranged in order of increasing atomic weights. In the cases of a few pairs of elements such as potassium and argon, iodine and tellurium, the element of higher atomic weight had to be placed first in the pair to fit its own family. Later this irregularity was explained by the occurrence of heavier isotopes of the element put in the leading position.

Modern Periodic Table: In 1913 the chemist Mosely studied the X-rays emitted by metal targets bombarded by cathode rays and suggested that a better periodic table would be based on the order of atomic numbers of the elements. This is the foundation of the present table. The elements are arranged in order of increasing atomic number from the lightest element hydrogen to the newer man-made radioactive elements of atomic number greater than 100. In the table, elements of the same chemical family occur in the same column or side by side.

Ia	2a	3b	4b	5b	6b	7b	8b	8b	8b	1b	2b	3a	4a	5a	6a	7a	O
1 H																1 H	2 He
3 Li	4 Be											5 B	6 C	7 N	8 O	9 F	10 Ne
11 Na	12 Mg											13 Al	14 Si	15 P	16 S	17 Cl	18 Ar
19 K	20 Ca	21 Sc	22 Ti	23 V	24 Cr	25 Mn	26 Fe	27 Co	28 Ni	29 Cu	30 Zn	31 Ga	32 Ge	33 As	34 Se	35 Br	36 Kr
37 Rb	38 Sr	39 Y	40 Zr	41 Nb	42 Mo	43 Tc	44 Ru	45 Rh	46 Pd	47 Ag	48 Cd	49 In	50 Sn	51 Sb	52 Te	53 I	54 Xe
55 Cs	56 Ba	57-71	72 Hf	73 Ta	74 W	75 Re	76 Os	77 Ir	78 Pt	79 Au	80 Hg	81 Tl	82 Pb	83 Bi	84 Po	85 At	86 Rn
87 Fr	88 Ra	89-103															

Lanthanides	57 La	58 Ce	59 Pr	60 Nd	61 Pm	62 Sm	63 Eu	64 Gd	65 Tb	66 Dy	67 Ho	68 Er	69 Tm	70 Yb	71 Lu
Actinides	89 Ac	90 Th	91 Pa	92 U	93 Np	94 Pu	95 Am	96 Cm	97 Bk	98 Cf	99 Es	100 Fm	101 Md	102 No	103 Lw

Periodic Law: When the elements are arranged in order of increasing atomic number a periodicity of chemical and physical properties occurs.

Periods: Each horizontal row in the periodic table is called a period. The first short period contains the elements hydrogen and helium in which the K shell is filled up to its maximum electron capacity of two. In the second short period from element 3, lithium to neon the L shell fills up in order to its maximum capacity of eight electrons. The next period contains a distinct series, the first transition elements from scandium (Z = 21) to zinc (Z = 30). The ten metals in this series fill up the d level of the L shell until the maximum of 18 second shell electrons is reached. Elements 39, yttrium to 48, cadmium form a similar transition series in which d electrons of the fourth shell fill in. The element lanthanum, number 57 and the following 14 elements form a very similar family called the lanthanides or rare earths. In this series electrons fill into the f-type levels of the fourth shell. Then from hafnium, number 72 to mercury, number 80 another transition series fills with d electrons.

In the seventh row an interesting family is the actinides from actinium, element 89 on. This series contains the important elements uranium and plutonium and other radioactive elements. Most members are man-made.

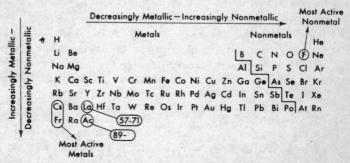

Groups Some of the chemical families occur as vertical groups in the table. The alkali metals, group I, and the halogens, group VII are usually studied as typical families.

Alkali Metals: These are the very active metals of group IA, and each from lithium to francium has one valence electron in the outermost shell corresponding to the group number.

The atomic size increases in going down the family from lithium to francium so that there is increasing ease of loss of the outer valence electron and therefore increasing metallic character. A typical property of metals is that they lose electrons and form positive ions. Expressed another way, there is a decrease of ionization energy from lithium to francium.

The halogen family members each have 7 electrons in the outer shell and are very active nonmetals in tending to gain an electron to complete the outer octet. Fluorine is the most active, and therefore the most nonmetallic because its outermost shell is closest to the attractive force of the nucleus and it gains the needed electron more readily.

Other families such as group IIA, the alkaline earths show similar chemical properties within the family, and gradual changes in physical properties.

Subgroups usually show little similarity other than common valences. Example: the subgroup IB containing copper silver and gold does not particularly resemble group IA.

Group O contains the inert (noble) gases in which most members show no tendency to form compounds. Another important group, number VIII, has the metals iron, nickel, and cobalt with similar properties side by side in the table. Similarly, the two groups of three metals directly below are also alike.

General Trends in the Periodic Table:

Francium is classed as the most metallic element, and a move in any direction in the table away from francium results in a decrease in metallic characteristics. Fluorine has the greatest electron affinity and electronegativity associated with nonmetallic character, and a move in the table in any direction away from fluorine leads to decreasing nonmetallic behaviour.

In going down a group as for example, group IV there is an increase in metallic character as the size of the atom increases and the ease of loss of electrons also increases. Carbon at the top of group IV is definitely a nonmetal, and lead at the bottom is a metal. Elements in a group show an ionic valence corresponding to the group number in the case of metals to the left side of the table. Examples: sodium in group IA has 1 electron in the valence shell and readily loses it to form the sodium cation Na^+ with valence +1. Calcium in group IIA forms the ion Ca^{2+} with valence +2.

At the other side of the table the nonmetal chlorine in group VII shows an electrovalence of $7-8 = -1$. Oxygen in group VI shows an ionic valence of $6-8 = -2$, that is the difference between the group number and the stable octet number 8. However elements may show other valences not directly related to the group number.

The table is generally useful in helping us predict the properties of an element knowing where it is located in the table but there are also defects. No table of the elements has yet been devised to show cross relationships between elements in different groups as for example, copper and mercury are similar but occur in different groups. Also, hydrogen does not particularly fit with any group although it shows similar valence and properties to some other elements.

NOTES

Don't forget to match that tough textbook with helpful

COLES NOTES

Expertly written, fast review summaries designed to give a greater understanding of the subject.

Shakespeare
Antony and Cleopatra
Antony and Cleopatra in
  Everyday English
Antony and Cleopatra — Ques. and Ans.
As You Like It
Coriolanus
Cymbeline
Hamlet
Hamlet in Everyday English
Hamlet — Ques. and Ans.
Julius Caesar
Julius Caesar in Everyday English
Julius Caesar — Ques. and Ans.
King Henry IV — Part 1
King Henry IV — Part 1
  — Ques. and Ans.
King Henry V
King Lear
King Lear in Everyday English
King Lear — Ques. and Ans.
Macbeth
Macbeth in Everyday English
Macbeth — Ques. and Ans.
Measure for Measure
Merchant of Venice
Merchant of Venice in Everyday English
Merchant of Venice — Ques. and Ans.
Midsummer Night's Dream
Midsummer Night's Dream in
  Everyday English
Midsummer Night's Dream
  — Ques. and Ans.
Much Ado About Nothing
Othello
Othello — Ques. and Ans.
Richard II
Richard III
Romeo and Juliet
Romeo and Juliet in Everyday English
Romeo and Juliet — Ques. and Ans.
Taming of the Shrew
Tempest
Twelfth Night
Winter's Tale

Shakespeare Total
Study Editions
Hamlet
Julius Caesar
King Henry IV — Part 1
King Lear
Macbeth
Measure for Measure
Merchant of Venice
Othello

Richard II
Romeo and Juliet
Taming of the Shrew
Tempest
Twelfth Night

Reference
Develop Your Memory Power
Dictionary of Literary Terms
Effective Term Papers and Reports
English Grammar Simplified
Handbook of English Grammar
  and Composition
How to Write Good Essays
  and Critical Reviews
Secrets of Studying English

Poetry
Frost's Poetry Notes
Gawain Poet
Keats' Poetry Notes
Paradise Lost
Poetry of Irving Layton
Rape of the Lock
Wordsworth's Poetry Notes
Works of John Donne
Yeats' Poetry Notes

The Canterbury Tales
Canterbury Tales
Prologue to the Canterbury Tales T.S.E.
Prologue to the Canterbury Tales
Wife of Bath's Tale

French
Contemporary French Literature
French Grammar — Ques. and Ans.
French Grammar Simplified
French Verbs Fully Conjugated
French Verbs Simplified

German
German Grammar — Ques. and Ans.
German Grammar Simplified

Spanish
Spanish Grammar — Ques. and Ans.

History
History of Canada
History of Great Britain
History of the United States
Outline of the Industrial Revolution
  in Europe
Outline of the Revolutionary Era
  in France

Geography
Africa, Australia, and
  South Pacific Islands (large)
Asia (large)
Canada and United States
Europe (large)
North and South America (large)
Physical and Human

Mathematics
Elementary Algebra Notes
Secondary Sch. Maths 1
Secondary Sch. Maths 4
Senior Algebra Notes

Chemistry
Elementary Chemistry Notes — Revised
How to Solve Chemistry Problems
Introduction to Chemistry
Senior Chemistry Notes — Revised

Physics
Elementary Physics Notes
How to Solve Physics Problems
Senior Physics Notes

Biology
Biology Notes

Sociology
Anthropology — Ques. and Ans.
Sociology

Philosphy
Philosophy — Ques. and Ans.

Psychology
Introductory Psychology
Psychology
Psychology — Ques. and Ans.

Literature
Adventures of Huckleberry Finn
Adventures of Tom Sawyer
All Quiet on the Western Front
Androcles & The Lion, Major Barbara
Animal Farm
Arms and The Man/
  Caesar and Cleopatra
Bleak House
Brave New World/
  Brave New World Revisited
Brothers Karamazov
Candide
Catch 22
Catcher in the Rye, Nine Stories